VOLUME
1

Originally published in the United Kingdom in weekly parts **COMBAT & SURVIVAL** is a study of the armed forces at work. It shows the skills taught to soldiers and the way in which military units operate. It examines the weapons and equipment used by different armies; and, by looking at recruit training and exercises, **COMBAT & SURVIVAL** demonstrates how the armed forces develop individual responsibility, leadership and initiative.

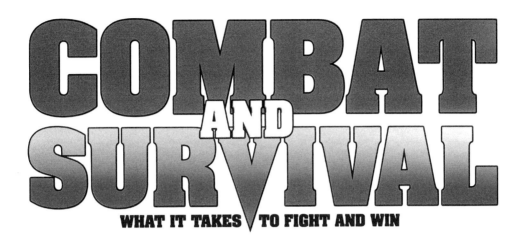

COMBAT AND SURVIVAL

WHAT IT TAKES TO FIGHT AND WIN

VOLUME
1

H. S. STUTTMAN, INC. *publishers*   Westport, Connecticut 06889

Published by H. S. STUTTMAN INC.
Westport, Connecticut 06889
© Aerospace Publishing 1991

ISBN 0-87475-560-3

INTRODUCTION

There are dozens, possibly hundreds, of military histories readily available to students of modern warfare. But for the reader interested in what goes on inside the world of the professional soldier – very little information has been made public.

That's why **Combat and Survival** was created. It is a unique study of the world's armed forces at work, depicting the hard reality of modern warfare. Step-by-step illustrations and guidance in personal military skills, military tactics, weapons handling and unarmed combat are complemented by sections on basic combat and survival techniques, plus a full review of the weaponry and hardware available to the modern soldier.

Combat and Survival is designed to show how men are trained to become expert fighters; how ingenuity and initiative are recognized and encouraged to produce engineers, teachers, leaders; what choices of weapons and equipment should be used in battle, when and why, and how technical skills can be developed to use them expertly; how individual responsibility becomes ingrained in every soldier and how it affects his every move; how personnel can be maintained at maximum fitness and preparedness levels – for whatever exotic climate or dangerous obstacles that will face them – through training and exercises.

Combat and Survival is not just *about* the techniques of making war – it is an authoritative military manual. It is wall-to-wall, hard "gutsy" facts written by men who know how to communicate successfully, in down-to-earth, easily understood language – yet with all the necessary technical information and military terminology left in.

And because it's a manual, it offers step-by-step guidance in personal military skills, military tactics, weapons handling and unarmed combat techniques. That means, while you're reading you're also learning what professional soldiers know about fighting – including information about the weapons and hardware available to them.

Each volume is profusely illustrated in color with large, clear action photographs and graphic drawings that open up weapons and equipment for complete examination and understanding. And the words and pictures keep perfect pace with each other – you always know exactly what you're looking at.

To gain the deepest possible insight into the world of the professional soldier, we have relied in large measure upon the experiences of the British armed forces, whose combat and survival skills are finely tuned from fighting in seventy-four shooting wars since the end of World War II – and whose personal combat and survival skills are renowned. And we have drawn on the combat and survival experience of the United States, NATO and Russian forces as well. Consequently, to retain the authenticity of the material, much of the language used throughout this remarkable series is British in origin and usage.

Unlike conventional books about warfare, **Combat and Survival** has developed a technique for showing many theatres and activities of military events happening at the same time. Each volume is designed to give the reader a broad view of simultaneous action. A battle could be fought by Special Forces in a mountain area, for example, while an infantry platoon is stalking the enemy in a steamy, far-off jungle – yet a battalion of armored vehicles could be advancing on still another front.

To reinforce this impression of simultaneous action and for greater appreciation and understanding of the subject, each volume covers five separate areas of combat and survival expertise: **Combat Skills; Weapons and Equipment; Survival; Unarmed Combat** and **Fighting Fit**. Interspersed throughout these five subject areas are personal recollections of heroic conduct in a series of **Combat Reports**. These narratives describe in the words of actual combat veterans the horror and devastation of modern warfare.

> **COMBAT SKILLS** explains military techniques, concentrating on small unit tactics, particularly those used by Special Forces units. The text is complemented by clear diagrams and photographs to illustrate everything from setting ambushes, sniping, assaulting enemy-held buildings, and patrolling day and night. Defense is not neglected. Included is material on defending positions against all threat levels from enemy raiders to armored assault by massed tank battalions. Terrain and climate are major influences on military operations and **Combat Skills** covers the special skills demanded by arctic warfare and action in mountains, jungle and desert.

WEAPONS AND EQUIPMENT provides full details on pistols, rifles, machine guns, anti-tank weapons and the special purpose weapons developed for anti-terrorist and clandestine operations. All significant armored vehicles are included from the latest Soviet tanks to the new generation of American combat vehicles which take armored warfare into the next century. Ground support aircraft like the US A-10 and Soviet Su-25 are compared and contrasted, and the use of the helicopter as a vital tool in offense and defense is fully covered.

SURVIVAL and the skills necessary to survive in the field have an outstanding tradition dating back to the Continental Army. This section covers everything from escape and evasion behind enemy lines to practical tracking and hunting techniques that help sustain life in the wilderness – even to building bone and stone tools! For long-term survival without modern equipment, the soldier must rely on ingenuity and initiative.

UNARMED COMBAT illustrates step-by-step instructions on how to deal with life-threatening situations using whatever comes to hand. The work includes a series of lessons in basic self-defense drawn from the combat manual of the British Royal Marines. Based on street fighting techniques, it is combat-proven and has been copied by Special Forces units all over the world.

FIGHTING FIT provides an inside look at the training programs of the world's toughest fighting units. From the U.S. Navy Sea Air Land (SEAL) teams and Army Rangers, to the British Royal Marines and Parachute Regiment and the Soviet *Spetsnaz* commandos.

COMBAT AND SURVIVAL is a complete manual of military techniques that brings the reader *inside the world of the professional soldier*. It is a study of the armed forces at work and shows the skills taught to soldiers and the way in which military units operate. It examines the weapons and equipment used by different armies; and, by looking at recruit training and exercises, **Combat and Survival** demonstrates how the armed forces develop individual responsibility, leadership and initiative. Unquestionably the skills of the soldier are a valuable study – democracy has no better safeguard than a well prepared people able to defend themselves.

THE PUBLISHERS

Contents

Volume 1

US SPECIAL FORCES: INSERTING TROOPS

Special Forces teams take the battle to the enemy on his own ground. Working behind the lines, their missions can vary from intelligence gathering to sabotage and organising guerrilla resistance movements against the enemy. It is a war without rules. The Special Forces soldier can expect no mercy from the enemy if he is caught: it is kill or be killed.

Many of the operational techniques are made up on the spur of the moment, to take advantage of a special piece of intelligence or some unexpected opportunity, but that doesn't mean there's no formal training. The military forces of the United States of America all have their special detachments, and they all take as their guide FM 31-20, the US Special Forces Operational Techniques field manual, on which this article is based.

Because they are 'Special Forces', their job is impossible to describe without listing all the possibilities. It's safer to say that as a member of a Special Forces team, you have to be prepared to tackle just about anything that comes up. You may be able to get back-up from technical specialists, but perhaps only in the form of a hurried, whispered radio conversation with a faceless person back at the operational base.

Most of the time, it will be impossible to say whether you're in attack or defence. You'll be conducting a guerrilla war. No front lines, no organised advance from one place to another, no start and finish lines.

Much of the Special Forces' job is taken up

US Special Forces are trained to fight behind enemy lines, raiding supply dumps and communications centres as well as organizing guerrilla movements for unconventional warfare. Their weapons are as specialized as their missions: this is a **5.56 mm Colt Commando** automatic carbine.

INFILTRATING SPECIAL FORCES TEAMS

When preparing a team for infiltration by parachute, remember the following:

1. Aircraft load capacity may limit the equipment and personnel you can take.
2. The presence of a reception committee on the drop zone makes 'sterilizing' the area and hiding your parachutes less of a problem.
3. You must ensure you take the equipment needed for your initial tasks.
4. The detachment commander places himself in the best position within the stick for controlling the team.
5. Team recognition signals and signals for contacting the reception committee must be decided in advance.
6. The primary assembly point should be 100 to 200 metres from the drop zone and you should have a secondary point 5 to 10 km from the DZ for use in an emergency.

A US Special Forces detachment is dropped into the sea by a low-flying helicopter. They will swim ashore with all their equipment, leaving no trace of their secret arrival.

through the identity checks, searches and interrogation, you will be able to live quite openly in enemy territory, not having to run and hide every time there's an unexpected knock on the door. Of course, you'll be living a double life and this will be stressful in itself, but then no-one ever said that Special Forces work would be easy, and certainly not safe!

Clandestine insertion means entering the enemy's territory without his knowledge. It could mean trekking across a border in a remote and difficult part of the country, or para jumping from an aircraft from almost seven miles up, and waiting until you're just a hundred or so metres above the ground before opening your parachute.

Or it may be struggling with all your equipment through the 64-cm diameter access hatch of a fleet submarine and swimming five miles through the dark to land on a deserted beach.

Air infiltration

Insertion from an airborne operation is popular because no area is inaccessible by air; it's quick; and, when organised properly, minimises the risk both to the carrier and to the passenger and his reception committee. There are three normal variants:
1 Low and normal altitude parachute
2 High altitude low opening (HALO) parachute
3 Air landing operations

The object of the exercise is to insert

with intelligence gathering and instruction, providing a 'cadre' of experienced leaders who pass on their knowledge to people recruited locally. Not that all of that knowledge is military. It can just as well be about personal hygiene or farming methods – anything, in fact, that proves to the local population that you and your country have their best interests at heart.

Winning the battle for the hearts and minds of the people is really much more important than taking an objective by armed force, but you can't win either of them until you get to the battlefield itself. Inserting agents into hostile territory has been a front-line intelligence task for hundreds of years, and there are two main methods:
1 False identities and disguise
2 Covert operations

Even in time of war, it is usually possible to gain access to the enemy's territory from a neighbouring country. The success of this method depends on the quality of your cover and documentation.

The biggest advantage of this approach is that once you have got

Special Forces troops set explosives to destroy a bridge: part of the team sets the charges while a third man keeps watch in the background. Note the mixture of US and Soviet rifles. Special Forces soldiers must be trained in all types of infantry weapons.

CLANDESTINE PENETRATION

HALO (High Altitude Low Opening) is a parachute technique used by Special Forces to arrive behind enemy lines without being detected. The aircraft flies at up to 8,000 metres; so high that it cannot be seen or heard from the ground. The troops free-fall most of the way down, linking up mid-air so they land in a tight group and only deploying their chutes when they are within 300 metres of the ground.

Keith Fretwell

Fast exit
All jumpers must exit the aircraft quickly and together so they can manoeuvre and free fall in a tight group and land without undue dispersion.

Reserve parachute
Guard your reserve parachute very carefully while you are on board the aircraft: if it deploys accidentally before you jump, it could stall the aircraft or try to pull you out through the side of the plane. A mistake here could spell body bags all round.

Reduced vulnerability
The idea behind HALO is to minimise the time that you spend floating slowly down on your parachute, which is your period of maximum danger from enemy fire and observation.

Tree jumping
As a technique for insertion into a jungle environment, this has been abandoned due to excessive casualties in Borneo and Malaya. You cannot expect to be able to jump directly into a tropical jungle without a lot of injuries.

Altimeter
Positioned on top of the reserve chute, this indicates your height above ground. At all costs check that this is in working order before you jump: at night it is your only means of knowing when to pull your chute.

Rifle protection
Tape over the muzzle to prevent dirt getting into the barrel when you land, and tape the handguards together to make sure they stay up. Cover all sharp edges to prevent personal injury in case of a bad landing.

Rucksack
The rucksack is rigged below your main parachute and is released on a lowering line when you are on your final approach to the drop zone

Waiting for the Viet Cong; in Vietnam US Special Forces played the enemy at his own game by inserting small teams into the jungle and ambushing the guerrillas.

the DZ after use? Are suitable aircraft available? Helicopter or fixed wing?

Landing from the sea

You must consider many of the factors that affect airborne insertions when planning an infiltration operation from the sea. First of all, what sort of coastal areas are available and what is the depth and efficiency of coastal defences? Do you have the right sort of marine craft to hand? Do you have the facilities to make sure that sea water can't effect vital pieces of equipment?

Submarines, because they are very difficult to detect when used properly, are very attractive as delivery vehicles, especially when the agents to be delivered can exit underwater and stay that way right up to the beach.

Land operations

Infiltration overland is very similar to a long-range patrol in enemy-held territory, and can be the most secure way of all of getting the Special Forces team into place, especially if time is not all-important. Distance is not necessarily a problem to fit, well-equipped Special Forces personnel, trained to use all their skills, wits and resources.

Where you can get help and assistance from 'friendlies' already in place, to provide food, shelter and intelligence, overland infiltration is

A utility boat brings Special Forces soldiers near the coastline in an inflatable dinghy. Once ashore they must deflate and conceal the dinghy before moving inland.

often the most effective of all. Because drop zones and landing zones are unlikely to be right next door to the area of operations, both air- and seaborne insertions will probably end up as overland journeys anyway. So there's a lot to be said for relying on your own two feet rather than on technology: man can escape detection a lot more easily than a machine.

One factor is common to all three methods of insertion that we've looked at so far – the availability of people on the ground to act as porters and guides and to provide security for the infiltrators. But it may not always be that way. In some cases the mem-

agents without the enemy's knowledge, so his capabilities as well as your own have to be taken into consideration. How good are his radar and air traffic control systems? Do adequate drop and landing zones exist? Are there personnel on the ground who can act as a reception committee, and help to transport people and supplies to safe locations and 'sterilize'

AREA DROP ZONE

An area Drop Zone is used by long range patrols who cannot guarantee their exact location when a pre-planned supply drop is due. The aircraft arrives at point A and proceeds to point B, looking for DZ markings on the way. The distance between the two points should not exceed 25 km and sites should be within 1 km of the line of flight.

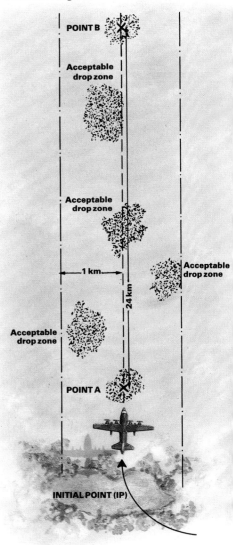

Aerial re-supply for an isolated Special Forces camp deep in the central highlands of South Vietnam. By arming and leading native tribesmen, the Special Forces inflicted serious damage on the Viet Cong.

bers of your team will have to go in blind, relying exclusively on your own skills and resources – not to mention a degree of luck!

Blind drops

These 'blind drops' are obviously very risky affairs, though probably not through exposure to enemy intelligence. After all, no-one will know you're coming, so there won't be a hostile reception committee at the DZ, either.

Blind drops are usually only made into areas that are known to contain a fair number of possible recruits – unarmed and untrained, probably, but providing the raw material for a strong indigenous operation. It may also be necessary to drop blind into areas where enemy security is tight and locals find it difficult to move around at will.

Staying behind

There is a fourth way of getting members of a Special Forces team into enemy-held territory – install them before the enemy moves in and takes over. Long-range planning and intelligence will dictate whether this is a real possibility

Keeping security will be the most

difficult part of the whole operation. Safe houses and refuges will need to be set up, communications established, caches of rations, arms and equipment made, and all without anyone outside the organisation having the faintest idea of what is going on. Members of Special Forces are trained to camouflage and conceal themselves superbly; to move silently; to live in the countryside without giving

themselves away. In towns and cities this is impossible, and so you must rely on the local people to provide security and communications, and probably rations and other supplies too – and that's all before you attempt any sort of operation!

Members of the US 7th Airborne Special Forces Group: demolitions experts, communications specialists and instructors in guerrilla warfare techniques.

Combat Report

Vietnam:
Saigon River Patrol

Dick Marquis, a US Navy Lieutenant with RAF-24 (River Assault Group), was part of the 3rd Navy Riverine Force working in the III Corps area on the Saigon River in Vietnam between March 1970 and March 1971.

Some Naval officers took the riverine course at Vallejo, California, where they were trained in PBRs (small, fast patrol boats), but my only training was 13 weeks of adviser school in San Diego. Until then, I'd been on nothing smaller than a destroyer and in training we were never even aboard a boat!

After arriving in Vietnam I rarely saw a PBR. One of our boats, which we called the "Zippo Lighter", was an LCM-8 (converted landing boat) with a flamethrower fired from a turret.

I was an adviser to the South Vietnamese, who were running supplies and material up the river on barges. Our main problem with the Viet Cong came at trouble spots like Ben Suc at the north end of the AO (area of operations): the river was very narrow here and Charlie was in a superb position to ambush us.

The Naked Firefight

We were supposed to have artillery support from FSBs (fire support bases) if Charlie tried to interfere with our yachting activities, but the support wasn't always there and we almost never had any air support. We were in many actions, but the one I'll never forget was The Naked Firefight, which took place in about July 1970.

We were escorting three supply barges under tow. Our convoy consisted of food and supplies that were badly needed by the ARVN (South Vietnamese Army) troops just north of us. I was on the back of an LCM, helping out but relying upon the South Vietnamese commander on the lead LCM to handle the situation if trouble arose.

It was about 4 p.m. We had stopped to give the men a short break and were having a swim; there were about a dozen American sailors and 40 Vietnamese in our convoy and nearly all of them were splashing around in the water.

Besides myself, there was the Vietnamese commander and an American FSO (fire support officer), who was supposed to call in artillery if we needed it. The FSO was standing next to me on the fantail of the LCM with his Prick Ninety (AN/PRC-90 field radio) lying nearby. I was watching the guys swim and splash when the FSO said, 'Trouble!'

A solitary B-40 rocket came in overhead,

hissing and sparking, and exploded with a dull crunching sound dead-centre on one of the barges. The concussion was terrific. Then we heard voices and more B-40 rockets started hissing around us.

'Up on the bank!' the FSO said to me. He pointed towards a stretch of elephant grass along the river where a whole bunch of VC were coming at us.

A solid wall of noise

At the same time, Charlie was lobbing mortars in on us. With the crump-crump of exploding mortar shells, the hiss of those rockets, and the noises made by the VC rushing at us – to say nothing of the shouting and confusion of our men – the whole stretch of river was just a solid wall of noise.

Their mortar fire was devastatingly accurate. In the first few seconds we lost a boat, which was lifted out of the water: everything shot into the air, mud and fish and dirt came raining down on us, but the boat itself simply disappeared.

The VC were ripping off at us with everything they had and our unclothed sailors were scrambling aboard the boats to get their weapons. The FSO got on the radio to call in fire and there was some confusion with callsigns. It went something like this:

'We need a fire mission *toute de suite*. Give us a couple, short, and we'll call the adjustments.'

'Who is this? Say again, how many VC are attacking you?'

'Can we have the rounds, please? We are under fire. Under fire.'

'Please say how many VC.'

'Many, many. They are firing on us. They are attacking us now, *right now*!'

'Please say how many VC are attacking you?'

'For Christ's sake, turn your radio over to somebody who can help us here. You want to know how many VC are attacking us. *There's a whole ******* full of the *******, that's how many!'

"Now you're gettin' 'em!"

I got myself into a higher and slightly more secure location on the boat and began squeezing off rounds at the VC with an M16 rifle, even though the distance was a little too great for accuracy.

Our own artillery – the South Vietnamese, actually – finally began coming in. It was exploding on the wrong side of the river pretty far from the VC but it seemed to slow them

The banks were close enough together for the VC to hit the boats from both sides.

down anyway. The FSO began arguing again with the artillery people. *'Will you put somebody on this radio who knows how to direct artillery fire?'* You always wondered, even in the middle of a firefight, why they sent you out here to do a job without being better supported.

Only a couple of metres from me, a burst of VC small-arms fire hit among three South Vietnamese sailors trying to scramble aboard. One man's head was blown apart in a red spray. That kind of thing happened, and you tried to forget it afterwards.

The VC were still coming at us when I saw what must have been one of the magnificent sights of the war. A sailor, a big muscular guy, got his hands on an M-60 machine-gun with the ammo belt dangling from it. He braced himself on the bow of the barge and began blazing away, totally naked.

Pretty soon, on all of our boats, naked men were firing away at the VC. Our artillery fire was finally beginning to fall in the general area of the VC. I went through several clips with my M16, sweating and shooting and cursing, and despite the distance I think I hit a couple of them.

'Now you're gettin' 'em!' I heard the FSO yell, and the artillery began to explode in the midst of the VC attackers. Now, they turned and ran for it. Our big, naked sailor stood up even higher, shooting his M60 from a hand-held stance.

'Come back here!' he shouted as Charlie started running off to fight another day. An hour after it had all started, by 5 p.m., the fight was over and the VC had withdrawn. They'd inflicted some casualties on us and blown one of our boats clean out of the water – but our supplies got through.

One of the most awesome sights on the Mekong Delta was a 'Zippo lighter': a landing craft fitted with flamethrowers and protected by improvized armor plate.

Combat Skills

RAIDS AND AMBUSHES

Special Forces units operate deep in the heart of enemy-occupied territory, undertaking both active and passive missions. A typical passive operation involves moving into position in the utmost secrecy, setting up a concealed and secure observation post, and then passing information about enemy troop strengths and movements back to HQ.

It may be months before the observers can be extracted or even re-supplied, so their training has to make them self-sufficient, allowing them to operate in the most hostile environments where one false move, day or night, could give the whole thing away.

Active operations such as raids and ambushes call for a different sort of courage. Daring instead of patience, decisiveness instead of caution. This second section on Special Forces Operational Techniques looks at the way active clandestine operations are planned and executed, and takes FM 31-20, the US Army's field manual for Special Forces, as its source.

A Special Forces raid is a surprise attack on enemy force or installation. It breaks down into four parts:

1 Clandestine insertion
2 Brief, violent combat
3 Rapid disengagement
4 Swift, deceptive withdrawal

Raids may be mounted to destroy enemy equipment and installations such as command posts, communications centres, and supply dumps; to capture enemy supplies and personnel; or simply to kill and wound as many of the enemy as possible. They may be used to rescue friendly forces or partisans, too, and can also serve to distract attention away from other operations.

Organizing the raid

The purpose of the mission, the type of target and the enemy situation will all have a bearing on the size of the raiding party. But whatever its size it will always have two basic elements – an assault group and a security group.

The assault group conducts the operation itself. They are the troops who go in and demolish installations, rescue the prisoners, steal the plans and code books or whatever the objective may be. As well as out-and-out fighting men, the group may include demolitions experts, electronics tech-

In the Vietnam war, Special Forces troops were used to play the guerrillas at their own game, small units of picked US troops raiding areas where the Viet Cong thought they were safe. Here, a US Navy SEAL takes cover by a VC bunker.

5 POINTS FOR A SUCCESSFUL AMBUSH

1. Set the ambush in a site you can move into and out of unobserved.
2. Use a night ambush if the mission can be accomplished by a short, intensive burst of fire.
3. Use a daytime ambush if a follow-up is required.
4. Choose a site where the terrain forces the enemy to bunch up.
5. Bear in mind that you may need a secondary ambush if enemy reinforcements can reach the scene quickly.

nicians, and whatever specialists may be needed – pilot, for example, if the object of the operation were to steal a specific enemy aircraft.

The security group is there to protect them, to secure the area and stop enemy reinforcements from becoming involved in the action, to stop any would-be escapers and to cover the withdrawal of the assault group.

Special Forces units have a well-deserved reputation for aggressiveness. Not one man amongst them will want to be idling away his time, and so they are always on the look-out for potential targets. Before operational planning can begin, each one is assessed for importance, accessibility and recoverability, taking into account distance and terrain and the strength of raiding party required.

Local repercussions

Another important factor is the likely effect on friendly natives and others as a result of the raid. There are countless examples of tens of local people being executed for every one occupying soldier killed. Planning for this possibility always forms part of the back-up organisation to the raid, and psychological operations experts (psyops) will also be ready to exploit any successes to the full.

Keep it simple

Although it should be accurate down to the last detail, the plan must be essentially simple. If success depends on a large number of factors coming together at the right time, any one of them going wrong will probably blow the entire operation.

Time – of day and of year – is a crucial factor in the plan. When the operation is straightforward and the physical layout of the target is well

US Navy SEALS (Sea-Air-Land) prepare to go ashore in the Mekong Delta and set up a night ambush. Their Tiger Stripe uniforms were developed from a North Vietnamese camouflage design.

known, it's probably better to operate during the hours of darkness. Where intelligence is less complete, go for dawn or dusk.

Withdrawal

Dusk is the best time for withdrawal; it gives you the advantage of the last minutes of daylight to exit the immediate area of the operation, and darkness to slow the enemy down during any follow-up. But in any event, choose the time very carefully to give yourself the greatest possible advantage.

It may seem obvious, but it's im-

possible to over-stress the value of accurate intelligence. There are three main sources:
1 Local agents
2 Reconnaissance
3 Satellite and high-level flights

Local knowledge is of the utmost importance. Whenever possible, friendly locals should be recruited to act as guides, and may even be employed in the raiding party itself if security considerations permit.

In the movement towards the objective, take every precaution so as not to alert hostile troops to your presence. Avoid contact, but make sure that the enemy suffers one hundred percent casualties if the worst does happen.

Test your weapons

Where conditions allow, conduct a weapons and equipment test before the assault phase, replacing any pieces of kit that may be faulty. Personal belongings should be 'sanitized' at the same time, even down to removing clothing labels if necessary.

Well defended objectives sometimes demand large raiding parties, perhaps in battalion strength or greater. Surprise is just as important as in a smaller raid, but will be much more difficult to achieve. A large raiding party will usually split into small groups and move towards the objective over a number of different routes. That way, even if some components are detected, the enemy may still be in the dark as to the real target.

Control and co-ordination of a large raiding party is more difficult, too, especially with regard to timing. Only

LAUNCHING A RAID

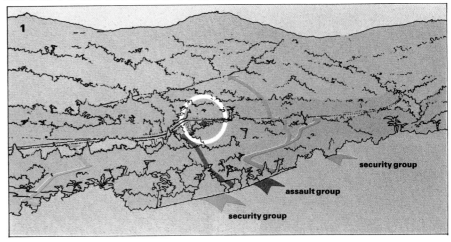

1 Whatever the mission and whatever the size of the raiding party, the principles of a guerrilla-style raid are the same. The actual assault team must be protected by security elements who will prevent enemy interference with the operation.

2 As the explosive specialist lays charges underneath the railway, on-the-spot security is provided by a small team of Special Forces soldiers. This team will take out any sentries on the objective, breach or demolish obstacles, and provide close protection for the main mission.

By taking out bridges, Special Forces raids block or delay the movement of enemy personnel or supplies, and by making certain routes useless they channel enemy movement on to a small number of major roads where it is more vulnerable to attack by other forces.

a high degree of training and excellent standards of equipment operation can make it easier.

Withdrawal after a large raid can be conducted with the party split up into small groups. This denies the enemy a large target for an air- or ground strike, but an alert and aggressive enemy may be able to mop up the force one unit at a time.

In some circumstances it is safer for the entire party to stay together and operate as a fighting column, but it will all depend on the situation of enemy forces, the terrain and the dis-

3 After the target has been destroyed the security groups provide cover on the flanks for the assault team to retreat. If the enemy follow the raiders, one security group should try to draw them away from the main assault force.

A NIGHT RAID

This is a typical night raid: blowing up the enemy's railway lines. Raids, especially if conducted at night, require meticulous planning and thorough rehearsal. Every member of the team should know exactly what he has to do where and when, and the 'O' Group (Orders Group, or briefing) should cover all eventualities. Rehearse everything, in the kit you will use on the job, preferably over similar terrain in a safe area. When planning the attack use all the available intelligence (INF), maps, air photographs, previous patrol reports and any locally-obtained INF. Practise in daylight, using the 'walk through talk through' technique; then do the whole thing again in silence.

Mission accomplished! A small team of commandos equipped with explosives can often strike strategic enemy targets more effectively than multi-million dollar airstrikes.

Cover group
While the demolition team is about its task, cover groups should provide flank, forward and rear protection.

Random frequency hazard
If you decide to electrically detonate the changes, be aware of RF hazard: your charges could be prematurely detonated by a radio transmission near your demolition circuit. You could avoid the problem altogether by using safety fuses, but this is not always tactically appropriate, so minimise the risk of keeping the radio well away from the demolition circuit.

Command detonation
The site from which you detonate the charge should be in good cover, overlooking the target and far enough away to be safe from the effects of the blast.

FRV (Final Rendez Vous) group
Pick an easily recognisable and defendable spot a few hundred metres away on the inward route to use as an FRV. You will withdraw here to regroup before you move off after the raid. Leave it secure with an FRV party, who will also provide rear protection. You may be able to leave Bergens in the FRV containing heavy kit you don't need for the raid.

Hot contact withdrawal
If you are attacked, you may have to withdraw to the FRV under fire. You should get away fast using fire and manoeuvre tactics. Discourage the enemy from following you by liberal use of white phosphorus, short-fused Claymores, other mines and booby traps. Make sure everyone knows the safe route out!

Camouflage
When laying the wire to the charges, take an indirect path following natural features or fence lines; a path of disturbed grass from the railway track to your position across an open field will be easily spotted from the air, and the chlorophyll from crushed grass shows an infra-red line scan (IRLS). If there is a continuous wire fence to the target you may be able to connect up to that.

Fire group
Make sure that the fire support group is in effective range for all its weapons. It may be necessary to clear vegetation from fields of fire, but don't remove too much or it may be noticed. Communicating between groups must be reliable, and if possible duplicated, i.e. radio and field telephone and perhaps a communication cord.

Radio
Don't use the radio until the attack is under way.

tances to be covered. An overt withdrawal, with no attempt at secrecy, will require a great deal of external support. There's very little chance that the extraction force, if there is one, will escape enemy attention.

Ambush

An ambush is a raid on a moving target. The only real difference is that the timetable of the operation becomes much sketchier and unreliable. Even excellent intelligence sources can't really predict the enemy's operational delays, and so the raiding party will often be in position for some time before the target comes along, considerably increasing the chances of detection.

Ambushes are conducted to destroy or capture enemy personnel and supplies or block their movement. A systematic approach can channel the enemy's communications and resupply operations, and force him to concentrate his movements on to main roads and railway lines, where they are more vulnerable to attack, especially from air strikes.

Railways themselves are always relatively open targets. Just removing the rails will bring the system to a halt. The attacking force tries to derail as many wagons and carriages as possible, and leave the wreckage blocking the track. This maximises the damage to stock, passengers and material, and slows down the work of repairing and reopening the permanent way.

Destroying the track

If the attack party is large enough they assault the train with automatic weapons and grenades. Part of the raiding party's security element will remove sections of track in both directions, some way away from the scene of the ambush. Explosive charges should be used to destroy the level rail-bed itself. This will prevent any possibility of reinforcements arriving unexpectedly.

Traffic on inland waterways – barges and smaller craft – can be disrupted in much the same way as railway trains, and the same technique is used against columns of vehicles on roads.

Combat Report
Vietnam:
Firefight at Hoa Long

Mike Glendon, who served with the 5th Royal Australian Regiment in Vietnam, describes his first firefight, in February 1969 at the village of Hoa Long.

Our platoon, a Long Range Reconnaissance Platoon or LRRP (pronounced 'LURP'), was to carry out a 'cordon and search' of Hoa Long village. We had been informed that the village was friendly towards us and we hoped it would stay that way, because it was about a mile and a half from our Task Force HQ.

Viet Cong personnel did their best to influence South Vietnamese villagers, and they would often move into a village at night and leave early in the morning. A cordon and search operation was an attempt to catch any VC that were around: by moving in at battalion strength in the early hours of the morning and surrounding the village, you could hopefully catch the enemy as they attempted to leave at daylight.

We were new to the country

We were to support Delta Company, which was to initiate the cordon with Alpha Company following the Bravo Company bringing up the rear as Tail End Charlie. Our platoon's job was to act as back-up if we were needed. There had been a rumour buzzing around for some time that something was in the air, and being called for a briefing the night before confirmed its truth.

Our saddle-up time was to be 3.30 am. The rest of that day was taken up in collecting our ordnance, ammunition, grenades etc; the Army likes to keep you busy before any engagement if it can. That night the talk was all about the action to come. I don't think we got much sleep – I know I didn't – and soon the familiar voice of Sergeant Godfrey telling us to saddle up rang in our ears.

We were new to the country and had trained for this for nearly a year; we were beside ourselves with excitement. Three hours later we were to discover the horror of a firefight.

Delta Company was at the jumping-off point at the Pearly Gates (entrance to the Task Force base at Nui Dat) along with elements of Alpha Company. After a short wait the move-out order was given: our first action in Vietnam had begun. I don't remember exactly how long we marched; I think it was about 1½ or 2 hours, most of which was in rice paddies and not on the road. That would have been inviting trouble if any VC were in the area, as the road was the main highway from Saigon going south.

Tracer bullets

After about two hours we were brought to a halt and told that we were waiting for Alpha and Delta Companies to get into position. Delta was to take the left flank and Alpha Company the right, with us filling the gap between them.

Eventually we moved up again and crossed the road, heading towards the village. Directly in front of me was a bank of earth about six feet high which ran down one side of the road on the same side as the village. Everything was going according to plan, or so it seemed.

But then tracer bullets started to come at us; they had a hypnotic effect, and it wasn't until I heard the crack of the automatic weapons that I realised what was happening. I couldn't work out why the tracer was red – I knew the Communist rounds had green tracers.

At this moment it seemed like the whole village opened up on us, and throughout it all I was frozen with fear. A sharp kick from my section leader telling me to move up brought me back to the horrific reality of what was happening.

Thank God for Army training

Being told to get up from the prone position where it is warm and safe and stand up and walk whilst under fire is quite unbelievable. Thank God for Army training: otherwise I would still be there, trying to dig a hole. Anyway, I got up and moved, as did the rest of the platoon.

We were in arrowhead formation, hopefully heading towards our support point for Alpha and Delta companies, but we were receiving so much fire at this stage that we had to go to ground. It occurred to me that none of us had returned any fire, so on the spur of the moment I opened up with my M16 and the rest of the platoon immediately followed suit.

At last we knew what a firefight was all about, and the feeling of power an automatic weapon in your hands gives you. But this was short-lived; a screaming lieutenant descended upon us, asking what the hell we thought we were doing, as we couldn't see what we were shooting at.

At this point two loud explosions occurred, and for two or three minutes everything went quiet. We didn't know what was going on, but we could hear the screams of a man in agony. We assumed it was a gook (VC). We were then ordered to move back and regroup on the road, which we did, and an hour later we were all moving back to Task Force HQ, tired and confused but proud that we had survived our first firefight. That's where we learned the horrible truth.

Hanging on the wire

The ARVN (Army of the Republic of Vietnam) – our allies – had an outpost at Hoa Long village, and they were the ones who had been firing on us as we approached. That was bad enough, but then we were told that one section – my section – had to go back to the village to reassure the villagers and the ARVN soldiers that it had all been a mistake. So off we went, with much moaning and bitching.

We arrived at the village at about 8 a.m. What we saw haunts me to this day. There, about 10 metres in front of us, hanging on the wire, were the bodies of Lieutenant Wilson and his sergeant. They had both stood on land mines that were surrounding the village. What hurt most was the fact that no-one had bothered to take the bodies down from the wire; that was left to us.

We shed our tears for these men – not only for the wasted lives, but because Lieutenant Wilson had been our platoon commander in training and believed in the Long Range Reconnaissance Platoon. He had become a friend to us all, and his friendship was and is still missed. I was to lose many more friends before Vietnam had finished with me.

We had been training for a year, preparing for action in Vietnam, and the Long Range Reconnaissance Patrol was to be the spearhead of the battalion. No-one expected the first firefight to happen the way it did.

SPECIAL FORCES AIRBORNE OPERATIONS

HIGH ALTITUDE LOW OPENING (HALO)

Use a visual ground marking system when there is good visibility.

1. **In HALO operations the Drop Zone markings show the impact point, not the release point.**
2. **The ground party must indicate wind direction and speed with flares or gas pots at night and panel markings in daylight, all formed as an arrow pointed into the wind.**
3. **Place markers at 25-metre intervals behind the arrowhead: one if the wind speed is 5-10 knots, two if it is 10-15 knots, and three if it is 15-20 knots.**
4. **The jump must be aborted if the wind speed is over 20 knots.**

The air is cold at 10,000 metres, with the hatch of the aircraft open and the wind strong enough to break the toughest grip. In the body of the aircraft the six-man HALO team crouch, every nerve tight. Suddenly the darkness is split by the red signal light on the bulkhead and the loadmaster taps the squad leader on the shoulder, sticking a thumb up in the universal sign for good luck.

The light pulses three times, goes out and is immediately replaced by green. All six men exit the plane as fast as they can.

For three minutes that feel like forever they dive through the night sky, each one searching the blackness below for the signal lights. Slowly they come into view, and each man traverses through the air until he's aiming at them.

The ground is close and coming up fast before they pull their cords, and the headlong rush gives way to a gentle glide into the landing site. Helping

Helicopters are an excellent means of inserting Special Forces troops and recovering them. Able to ascend and descend almost vertically, land on small plots of ground and to fly safely at low altitudes they are particularly valuable in jungle operations. On the other hand they are very noisy and have limited range.

Combat Skills

In Vietnam, US Special Forces teams led groups of tribal guerrilla fighters against the Viet Cong and were supplied by aircraft like the Caribou, which needs little room to take off and land.

hands release their harnesses and silent greetings are exchanged, and then they're off about their secret, deadly business.

Airborne operations are the arteries and veins of Special Forces operations in enemy-occupied territory. In most cases, it's just not possible to get men and supplies in and out of operational areas by any other means, and so a great deal of effort goes into making them as safe, secure and simple as possible. This section, taken from the US Army's handbook, introduces you to the methods that are used.

The first stage of any airborne operation is the identification and selection of Drop Zones (DZs) or Landing Zones (LZs).

Local intelligence

Before Special Forces teams are on the ground, they have to depend on local intelligence and information, maps, and aerial or satellite reconnaissance. As many sites as possible are ear-marked for further investigation after teams have been infiltrated, and everything that's known about them is filed away for future use.

One of the first tasks for the infiltration team is a survey of all the possible zones. Because as much detail as possible has been compiled previously, only small corrections will need to be transmitted by radio, to keep traffic to a minimum and maintain security. Any site that shows up badly will just be crossed off the list. More important still, it won't be necessary to transmit even coded map references; sites will always be identified by code names or

numbers, agreed in advance in the security of the operating base.

This cloak of secrecy, by no means unusual in Special Forces operations, is to ensure the security of DZs and LZs, by sites that are very vulnerable to enemy infiltration and surveillance or attack. If the zones' locations fall into enemy hands, not only is the immediate operation compromised, but it may lead to other friendly agents and sympathisers being captured too.

Air delivery operations

While the Special Forces Operations Commander has responsibility for selecting DZs and LZs, it's the air unit carrying out the mission that decides whether to use them or not. The aircrew are at a great deal of risk during these missions, and not just directly from enemy activity.

These air delivery operations are normally carried out by a single aircraft, flying at low level over difficult terrain, in conditions of poor visibility and making frequent changes of course – doing all the things that pilots normally go to any lengths to avoid, in fact. To make matters worse, they have to be pin-point accurate first time around – there's no chance for a second attempt.

The helicopter's ability to hover close to the ground allows troops to be inserted in forested areas where no landing zone can be found.

Selection of delivery zones

Drop Zones and Landing Zones must please both the aircrew who are to fly the mission, and the reception committee who will be there to meet the consignment and passengers. From the aircrew's point of view the zone should be easy to identify from above, and the countryside around it relatively free of obstacles.

Flat or rolling countryside is best, but if the Special Forces operation being supported is located in mountainous country, this may not be possible. In that case it's best to choose sites on broad ridges or plateaux. Small enclosed valleys or hollows, completely surrounded by hills, should be avoided whenever possible.

Open approaches

To give the aircrew as much flexibility as possible in the route they will take to the zone, it should be accessible from all directions. If an approach can only be made from one direction, then the area should be free of obstacles for five km on each side, to give the aircraft space to perform a 'flat turn'.

Hills more than 300 metres higher than the elevation of the zone itself shouldn't be closer than 16 km away when the site is to be used for night operations. In exceptional circum-

stances, where this sort of obstacle can't be avoided, the aircraft may be forced to fly higher than normal, and this may mean the consignment landing a long way from the DZ itself as a result of wind drift.

High wind is only one of the weather conditions that can affect the operation. Low cloud; mist and fog patches; still air where smoke may be present; and even heavy rain or snow – all these can interfere with the aircrew's ability to pick up visual ground signals.

Even particularly tall trees can be a potential danger to an aircraft doing a low-level drop. Where the operation is to take place at 130 metres or less, the safety requirements are that there should be no obstacle higher than 30 metres within 8 km, if possible. Where the aircrew have no choice but to put up with such obstacles in the immediate area of the DZ, their location must be well known.

The drop zone

The DZ should be equally accessible from all directions, so the best shape is round or square, even though the various packages that make up the consignment will land in a line parallel to the course of the aircraft. Dispersion – the distance between the points where each component will hit the ground – is mostly controlled by

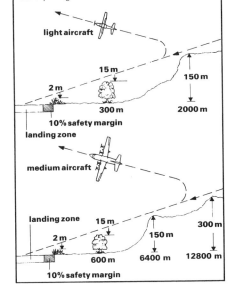

Take-off and approach clearances for fixed-wing aircraft

Minimum landing zone sizes
Light aircraft: 305 m × 15 m
Medium aircraft: 920 m × 30 m
Add a 15-metre cleared strip each side as a safety margin.

LEVEL TURNING RADIUS

1 The general area surrounding the drop zone must be relatively free from obstacles which might endanger the aircraft. Flat or rolling terrain is the best, but plateaux in hilly country can be suitable.

2 Small valleys surrounded by hills should not be used for drop zones.

3 For night operations you must avoid using drop zones with ground rising to 300 metres within 16 km of the site level.

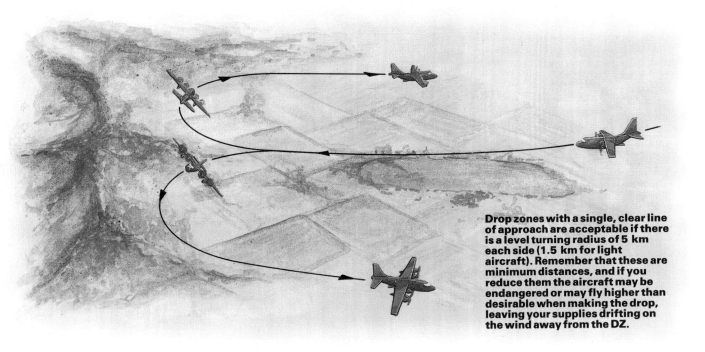

Drop zones with a single, clear line of approach are acceptable if there is a level turning radius of 5 km each side (1.5 km for light aircraft). Remember that these are minimum distances, and if you reduce them the aircraft may be endangered or may fly higher than desirable when making the drop, leaving your supplies drifting on the wind away from the DZ.

LANDMARKS AND WAY-POINTS

The further an aircraft has to fly on a compass course, without way-points (visual checks on position), the more likely it is to be off the correct course. The main causes are tiny inaccuracies in the compass and other instruments, and external factors such as wind.

Special Forces re-supply missions rely on being pinpoint accurate first time: the pilot hasn't time to fly around the countryside looking for the drop zone.

The usual procedure is to select an easily identified landmark somewhere between eight and 24 km away from the DZ itself. The pilot then takes his bearings from this point and flies on a compass heading for a predetermined time to bring the aircraft over the zone.

Features that stand out from the ground may well not make good landmarks from the air, especially at night. These are the sort of things you should be looking for:

1 Coastline in distinctive stretches, especially with breaking surf or white sand beaches, river mouths over 50 metres wide, or sharp promontories or inlets.
2 Rivers more than 30 metres wide. Heavily wooded banks will reduce their visibility.
3 Canals. Their straight course and consistent width make them easy to spot, except where the surrounding countryside follows a uniform pattern.
4 Lakes at least a square kilometre in area with a distinctive shape or feature.
5 Woods and forests a square kilometre and more in size, with clear-cut boundaries or some special identifying feature.
6 Major road and highway intersections
7 Railways, especially when there is snow on the ground.

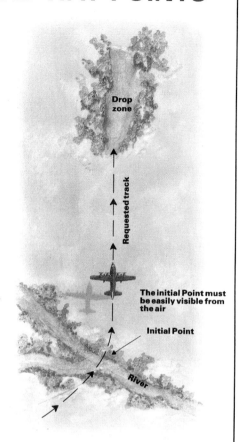

Drop zone / Requested track / The initial Point must be easily visible from the air / Initial Point / River

Above: Special Forces landings demand manoeuvrable parachutes. This rectangular aerofoil canopy enables you to keep a tight control on your direction and rate of descent.

Below: Securing the drop zone ready to receive air dropped supplies, US troops fan out across the selected site. Note their weak personal camouflage and the giveaway gold watch strap!

the speed of the aircraft over the ground, and the time it takes to get the whole consignment out through the hatch.

Dispersion

The rule of thumb for low-level operations is that half the speed of the aircraft in knots (nautical miles per hour; 100 knots 115 mph), multiplied by the time it takes to get the whole consignment out of the aircraft, will give the dispersion in metres on the ground.

This is the critical distance, because it determines how long the zone needs to be. If possible, add at least 100 metres at each end as a safety factor. Sometimes it may be impossible to find a potential DZ as wide as it is long that meets all the other requirements.

Drop zone axis

If you have to use an oblong DZ, it must have its long axis in absolutely the right direction to allow the pilot of the aircraft the best possible chance of completing his mission safely and delivering the consignment into the right hands. It must make some allo-

HOW TO SEND AN AIRDROP MESSAGE

Whenever you use a radio, keep the three principles of use in mind: **Security, Accuracy,** and **Discipline** (SAD).

Security
Remember the eternal triangle of sender, receiver – and enemy monitor. Keep your transmissions as short as possible, always encode your own and enemy grid references, and be careful not to use names or appointment titles on the radio. If in doubt, encode it into battle code (BATCO). Watch your speech mannerisms; these can also give you away and are a valuable source of long-term intelligence.

Accuracy
You must encode and decode accurately; BATCO leaves no room for mistakes. Corrections take up valuable seconds that could lead to a message being intercepted and a traumatic experience: for example, in a 40-second fire mission a battalion of Soviet BM-21 multi-barrelled rocket-launchers can deliver 14 tonnes of HE (high explosive) or chemical agent onto your position.

Discipline
You must obey radio net discipline, provide constant radio watch, and answer calls correctly and quickly. Use correct voice procedure, apply the rules of BATCO and this will help prevent enemy electronic warfare units from breaking in on your net.

You must be aware of your radio voice. It should differ from normal speech in the following respects: **Rhythm, Speed, Volume** and **Pitch** (RSVP).

1 Rhythm
Divide the message up into logical portions, and deliver it at an even rhythm with pauses; remember the recipient has to write it down.

2 Speed
BATCO delivered too quickly will lead to mistakes; delivery must be slightly slower than normal speech.

3 Volume
Speak slightly louder than normal, but don't shout; this just distorts the message.

4 Pitch
Try to pitch your voice slightly higher than normal; this enhances clarity.

A typical drop zone report

Your report might look like this:

Code name:
DZ HAIRY
Location:
THREE TWO TANGO PAPA TANGO SIX FOUR ONE TWO FOUR THREE
Open quadrants:
OPEN ONE THREE ZERO DEG TO TWO TWO ZERO DEG AND THREE THREE ZERO DEG TO ZERO ONE TWO DEG
Recommended track:
TRACK THREE SIX ZERO DEG

Obstacles:
RADIO TOWER ZERO EIGHT SIX DEG SIX KM

1 The **code name** would have been decided on and briefed prior to the mission.
2 The **location** of the centre of the drop zone is given as a partially encoded six-figure grid reference.
3 The **open quadrants** gives the boundaries of the drop zone. Note

Concealed in a treeline, a US Ranger team talks to circling American aircraft near the Cambodian border in 1970.

these are in degrees, not mils.
4 The **recommended track** is the approach route, again in degrees.
5 The aircraft would be warned of any potential **obstacles** and their position on or near the track.

---

wance for sidewinds, because this will dictate how far to the side of the aircraft's track the drops will land. It's not sufficient to expect the pilot to compensate completely for sidewinds by 'aiming off'.

The surface of the drop zone should be level and free from obstructions such as rocks, fences, trees and powerlines. Where personnel are to be dropped at high altitude (15,000 metres and higher), try to locate DZs in soft snow or grassland. Parachutes fall faster in the thin high air, and so the passenger will hit the ground harder.

Dangerous drop zones
Swamps and marshy ground, including paddy fields, are suitable both for personnel and bundles of goods in the wet season, and for bundles when they are dry or frozen. Water-covered DZs are particularly dangerous to heavily-laden personnel: in the airborne landings on D-Day in Normandy, for example, on 6 June 1944, the American 82nd and 101st Airborne Divisions lost so many men drowned in flooded fields that their combat

DISPERSION PATTERN

The first man or package out of the aircraft will obviously tend to land some distance behind the last man out. You can calculate the dispersion as follows: half the speed of the aircraft in knots, multiplied by the exit time in seconds, equals the dispersion distance in metres.

The dispersion distance is the absolute minimum length of the drop zone.

release point

forward throw

last bundle

first bundle

wind drift

release point marking panels

dispersion pattern

efficiency was badly reduced. They were carrying more than a normal equipment load.

It is possible to drop into water, providing special precautions are taken. The water should be at one and a half metres deep; it should be cleared of obstructions both on and below the surface; it must be 10°C or warmer; it must be free of swift currents and shallow areas and there must be a foolproof recovery system that en-

sures that personnel don't stay long in the water.

One particular problem that dropping into water minimises is that of cleaning up the DZ after use, so that no tell-tale signs of the operation are left. Be particularly careful when dropping on to agricultural land. If the fields in question are cultivated, it will be next to impossible to eradicate all traces of the drop.

Unarmed Combat Course No.1

by Peter Brown MBE, ex-Royal Marine Commando and 4th Dan (Black Belt) in Judo

PREPARE FOR ACTION

Most people's reaction to being threatened or attacked is panic or confusion. As a result they end up as victims, even if they fight back. But by staying calm and following a careful strategy of self defence it is possible to turn the tables on an attacker. With good judgement and a bit of luck you may even be able to defuse the situation without recourse to violence. But if you are forced to counter-attack, you must remember that unless you are in a combat zone you are still subject to the law.

The use of reasonable force

In war, there are few rules save those of survival. But in civilian life you must adhere to the well-established principle of common law that you can only use *reasonable* force to defend yourself against unjustified attack. Section 3 of the Criminal Law Act 1967 provides that a person may use 'such force as is reasonably necessary in the prevention of crime, or in effecting the lawful arrest of offenders or suspected offenders or of persons unlawfully at large'. But what constitutes 'reasonable force' is not spelt out – so if you use a degree of force that the police consider unreasonable, you could face prosecution.

Unarmed combat can cause serious injury or even death. If you go too far, you could face a charge of grievous bodily harm, or even murder or manslaughter. Likewise, the techniques should only be practised in the correct environment for learning and under a skilled instructor.

Practice makes perfect

Fast reflexes are very important in self defence; when the crunch comes you will not have time to think and prepare your moves. The only way to develop your reflexes is to practise with a compatible partner under proper supervision. You must practise until you can remain totally alert but with your muscles relaxed: tense muscles do not function so well.

Defensive Stance

When preparing to respond to an attack the body should move to a stance that is mobile and prepared for action.

The arms should be prepared to strike. At the same time, you should put on a cringing, fearful response so as to lull your opponent into a false sense of security. He is then more likely to present you with an opportunity to counter-attack.

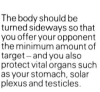

The body should be turned sideways so that you offer your opponent the minimum amount of target – and you also protect vital organs such as your stomach, solar plexus and testicles.

The base is important. Both feet should be placed shoulder width apart, with equal weight on each foot.

The feet should move in small steps so that you are within close striking distance of your attacker.

DEFENCE AGAINST KICKS

The kick is one of the most dangerous attacks you can face: the leg muscles are the strongest in the human body and can direct a foot or knee with great accuracy and force. It is therefore very important to learn how to defend yourself against such an attack. In this section we will deal with two situations: (1) defending yourself from the ground and (2) the shin check. Part 2 of the Unarmed Combat Course will look at how to floor an attacker who is attempting to kick you and how to perform a cross-arm parry.

Defending yourself when lying on the ground

You are at your most vulnerable if on the ground, and unless you react quickly and positively you are in trouble. Your responses should be as follows:

1 Protect your head from kicks by using your arms and protect your spine by lying on your back in a position in which you can swivel round easily.

2 Swivel round and use your legs to block a kicking action.

3 Block a kick with one leg and use your free leg to trip up the attacker.

THE FOUR PRINCIPLES OF SELF DEFENCE

Self-defence should always follow these four steps:

1 Prevention
It is far better to prevent an attack occurring at all rather than to defend yourself in a fight that you might not win. To do this you must use brain, not brawn, and decide whether you can resolve the situation without violence. It may not be possible, your opponent may not give you the option, but it can be worth a try.

2 Awareness
It is very easy to concentrate exclusively on what you are doing rather than pay attention to your local surroundings. This is a recipe for being ambushed. Do not wander near unsecured cover. Plan ahead and think through the route you will take. Your aim is to reduce the opportunities for a successful attack.

3 Release
Once you get used to thinking ahead and becoming aware of possible risks you will only have to concentrate on releases: techniques for use against different forms of attack. This series will show you a simple series of releases. You can gain time to work out a plan of action by showing no resistance at first: look humble and even grovel a bit. This can make an attacker over-confident and off his guard. If it does come to blows and the attacker is armed, deal with the weapon before the man.

4 Escape
Once released, you should take the first opportunity to escape and get out of danger. There is nothing to be gained by hanging about. Remember: throughout the confrontation stay calm and evaluate the situation as it develops.

Prepared for action
When faced with a dangerous situation, the body will automatically prepare itself for action using the 'flight or fight' response: hormones are released and the nervous system sends signals to all parts of the body. This triggers the following body responses:

1 Sweating increases – to help cool the body
2 Blood clotting ability increases – preparing for possible injury
3 Blood is diverted to the muscles, and muscle fibres tense – ready for action
4 Senses are activated – to make you mentally alert
5 Breathing rate speeds up – nostrils and the air passages in the lungs open up to let in more oxygen
6 The heartbeat speeds up, and blood pressure rises
7 The liver releases sugar, cholesterol and fatty acids into the blood to supply instant energy to the muscles
8 The bladder and bowel muscles close down.
Any non-essential activity ceases.
The body is now fully prepared for action.
And now you must prepare yourself to take appropriate action. Remember – keep *cool*, *calm* and *collected*.

The methods described in the Unarmed Combat Course are demonstrated by two Royal Marine Physical Training Instructors. The Marine with the dark hair and moustache represents the attacker, and the one with fair hair is the defender.

> **The first 6 parts of the Unarmed Combat Course are:**
> 1. **The principles of self-defence and two defences against kicks.**
> 2. **Defence against kicks and how to floor your attacker.**
> 3. **Defence against wristholds.**
> 4. **Armlocks and wristlocks.**
> 5 and 6. **How to escape from a hold.**

The shin check
This is a simple and effective technique for blocking a kick:

1 As the attacker kicks at you, turn your body to the side and bring the defending foot up (the foot nearest to the attacker).

2 Using the edge of your foot, stop the attacker's kick with a checking action applied to his shin. This is very painful and should incapacitate your attacker.

3 Alternatively, if you are carrying an object in your hands, this can be used to block the attack instead.

Unarmed Combat Course No. 2

FLOORING THE ATTACKER

If someone sets on you without warning, the chances are that he'll attack feet first, kicking viciously. So it's vital to know how to defend yourself properly against kicks and, if possible, to turn the tables on your attacker.

The simplest defence relies on very fast reactions: jump clear, and leave the attacker balancing – or not – on one leg. But he may be in too close, or come at you too quickly. So, in this section, we are dealing with more positive defences against a kicking assailant. They are:

Turn and lift

The turn and lift technique uses the principle of minimum force but with great effect: it uses the attacker's momentum against him.

Most attackers will kick with the right foot. If they happen to use the left foot, then use the same technique but on the opposite side.

1 The attacker runs towards you and at the last moment kicks in your direction.

2 Your immediate reaction should be to turn sideways, so as to offer the minimum target.

3 Then use your arm (not your hand) to cradle the attacker's leg and raise and carry on the momentum. This should send your attacker crashing onto his back and allow you to take the initiative.

Cross-arm parry

This is a simple technique to use when someone directly in front of you tries to kick you.

1 As the attacker kicks with his right foot, you must first place your most vulnerable body parts out of range by shifting your hips backwards.

2 At the same time, drive your arms down (your right arm on top) in the form of a cross and block the attacking leg.

3 Then, grasping the attacker's heel with your right hand, lift and turn his leg to get him off balance. This will expose him to follow-up action if necessary.

Using the kick as a defence

If the nature of the attack is so aggressive and determined that the initial defences are ineffective, you may be justified in using a single kick or blow with the knee to protect yourself. Naturally you must be the judge of this in the prevailing circumstances, and you should remember the principle of minimum force.

The foot or knee can be used very effectively in defence as follows:

1 The side kick
The side kick should be used whenever possible, as it enables you to reach further and put more downward force into the action.

2 The shin scrape
This is used when the attacker is holding you from behind. The knee is raised up and then the edge of the foot is driven down the attacker's shin and onto the small bones of his foot.

3 The snap kick
The knee is raised first in a powerful movement and the foot is then snapped forward against the attacker's knee or testicles.

4 The knee blow
This is also a very effective defence when you are being held from the front. The knee is brought up forcibly against the attacker's groin or stomach.

Unarmed Combat Course No. 3
DEFENCE AGAINST FRONT HOLDS

Turn and push away

If for some reason you're not able to stop an attacker grabbing hold of you, the next thing he'll do is try to force you to the ground. What you have to do is to stop him getting that far. This section of the Unarmed Combat Course shows several very simple and very efficient defences that should stop any attacker.

1 The attacker comes close to you and grabs you by the lapels, using both his hands.

2 Use your legs to make a sudden turn, and thrust your arm through the attacker's arms and on to his chest with great force.

4 Alternatively, if the attacker does not let go, you can use the same manoeuvre to deliver a finger strike to the attacker's eyes.

3 By turning sideways you extend your reach, enabling you to deliver a sudden, surprise blow.

Single arm swing and blow

1 The attacker comes in close and grabs the front of your chest with both hands.

2 Swing your right arm over as hard as you can to break the attacker's grip.

3 If the attacker still doesn't let go after you have brought your arm over, deliver an elbow smash to his head.

Both elbows over with head butt or knee strike

1 We start from the same position: the attacker has grabbed you by the lapels with both hands.

2 Bring your arms up high to take your elbows above his arms and break the grip.

3 If you cannot break his grip by this method you are well placed to deliver a head butt.

4 If you do not fancy trying a head butt, the same stance leaves you in a position to make a knee strike to the attacker's groin.

Unarmed Combat Course No. 4
DEFENCE AGAINST FRONT HOLDS PART 2

The three techniques described here all defeat a front hold by counter-attacking. In each method, you attack the assailant's face or head, taking advantage of the way he has grabbed you. But remember: as in all self-defence manoeuvres, you must bear in mind the principle of minimum force and never practise without trained supervision.

Drive both arms up and blow to nose

1 The attacker grasps you by your lapels.

2 Using your legs to give you thrust, drive your arms up between the attacker's arms, until your hands meet.

3 Then join your hands together and smash them down onto the bridge of the attacker's nose.

Trap attacker's wrist and strike with free hand

1 This time the attacker grasps your chest with a single hand.

2 The grasping hand is first trapped by your own forearm.

3 Then you turn your body to pull the attacker onto you. The free hand then carries out a chin jab.

Trap attacker's wrist and pull head through to wall

This defence is useful if you are attacked near a building or wall. But remember: if you use this defence, do not use more force than is necessary to protect yourself.

1 Once again the attacker grasps you with one hand.

2 The grasping hand is trapped with your opposite forearm.

3 Pass your free hand up and behind the attacker's head.

4 You then pull his head past you and through to the wall.

33

The UZI in Action

Brutally simple and easy to operate, the UZI sub-machine gun has established a powerful reputation in the last 30 years. In Israel it is practically a national symbol, armies in every continent have now adopted it, and it is used by US Special Forces. When John Hinkley tried to assassinate President Reagan in 1981 he quickly found himself on the wrong end of an UZI held by a US Secret Service agent.

The UZI is a very well-balanced weapon, which makes it comfortable to shoot both from the hip and the shoulder. Its stability helps make it accurate when firing in the single-shot mode and ensures that it is easy to control when firing on full auto. Another reason for the UZI's popularity is its reputation as a very dependable weapon: UZIs have been dropped in water, buried in sand and bounced down cliffs, yet they faithfully continue to function.

The UZI is named after its inventor, Lieutenant Uziel Gal of the Israeli army. When it was formally organised in 1948 the Israeli army was using a huge variety of weapons including German MP38s and MP40s, British Sten guns and Italian Berettas. Weapons training, maintenance and the supply of spare parts were a nightmare, and Gal settled down to design a new gun altogether. He studied every sub-machine gun he could get his hands on, comparing their strengths and weaknesses. He wanted, and the Israelis desperately needed, a gun that was reliable, compact and simple to manufacture.

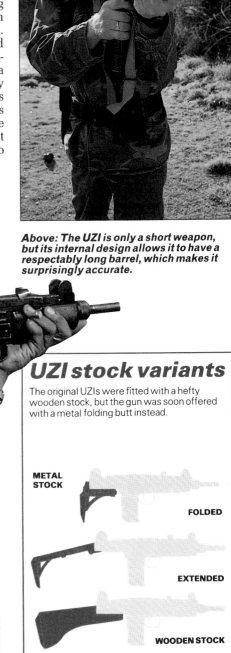

Seen here in South African hands, the UZI sub-machine gun can boast over 30 years of successful combat action. From a steady firing position and with the shoulder stock folded out, the UZI has an effective range of 200 metres, but it is really intended for close quarter fighting.

Above: The UZI is only a short weapon, but its internal design allows it to have a respectably long barrel, which makes it surprisingly accurate.

UZI stock variants

The original UZIs were fitted with a hefty wooden stock, but the gun was soon offered with a metal folding butt instead.

METAL STOCK

FOLDED

EXTENDED

WOODEN STOCK

With its awesome rate of fire and small size, the Mini-UZI is suitable only for point-blank range. A silencer is not only quieter but greatly improves accuracy.

Both UZIs take the same magazine, and a clip at the bottom allows you to connect two magazines into an 'L' shape; ideal for fast magazine changes.

The UZI's rearsight is flipped over to set it for either 100 or 200 metres, and when firing single shots from the prone position it is surprisingly accurate.

The grip safety in the trigger grip needs to be firmly squeezed or the weapon will not fire. This can be irritating if you are unused to it, but is not a serious problem.

US Special Forces use the UZI; and when the British SAS created their Counter Revolutionary Warfare Wing in the early 1970s they too chose the UZI for their assault team.

When it appeared the UZI was revolutionary. It was quickly recognised as a masterpiece of gun design and orders flooded in from armies around the world, keen to examine it for themselves. There were several reasons for this, but the most obvious was the convenient stubbiness of the UZI. The German MP40 sub-machine gun, often (but incorrectly) called the 'Schmiesser', was a first-class weapon, 68 cm long and housing a 25-cm barrel. Gal's UZI was just 47 cm long but had a 26-cm barrel.

Bolt governs size

To appreciate why the UZI was so revolutionary, it is necessary to understand how World War II sub-machine guns worked. Most were 'blowback' weapons, consisting of a barrel fitted into a body with a bolt sliding backwards and forwards in the body under the power of a spring. By cocking the gun you pulled the bolt back, compressing the spring. When you pulled the trigger, the spring was released, letting the bolt fly forward,

pushing a cartridge from the magazine into the chamber and firing it. The force of the explosion sent the bullet out of the barrel and also tried to blow the cartridge case backwards against the bolt.

The bolt was forced backwards by the explosion but, as it was heavier than the bullet and still travelling forwards when the bullet fired, there was a delay before the 'blowback' action began. This allowed the bullet to leave the muzzle and pressure to drop before the bolt began to move backwards. On its way back, the bolt extracted the empty cartridge case and ejected it. If you were still holding the

trigger back the bolt would then be driven forwards again by the spring and fire the next round.

The size of a gun like the MP40 was governed by the size of the bolt and the distance it had to recoil against the spring. A bolt had to be 10-12 cm long, recoiling for about 15 cm; thus from the rear of the barrel the gun body had to be at least 27 cm long.

'Wrap-around bolt'

Uziel Gal didn't like this. He wanted a short and handy gun which would be more convenient for Israeli tank crew, easily stowed in vehicles and ideal for Special Forces operations. One of the sub-machine guns he examined was the Czech Model 23 which had an unusual feature called the 'wrap-around bolt'. This was the answer: a rather longer bolt than usual, of which the forward two-thirds was hollow.

The barrel was fitted into the gun body so that it was unsupported inside the body, and thus when the bolt ran forward the hollow part 'wrapped around' the rear of the barrel until the bolt face met the chamber. Slots in the hollowed-out portion of the bolt allowed for feed from the magazine and ejection of the empty case.

The gun now consisted of a barrel which was largely inside the gun body; a long bolt of which only one-third was behind the breech at the moment of firing; and only sufficient space inside the gun body to allow the solid section of the bolt to move far enough back to permit extraction and feed through the slots.

Magazine housing

Uziel Gal adopted another idea from the Czech design: that of placing the magazine inside the pistol grip. Most sub-machine guns had their magazines well forward, where they were often useful as a second hand-grip, but putting the magazine in the pistol grip became necessary due to the short bolt movement and it also made changing magazines in the dark very much easier because you don't need to see to put your hands together.

To make manufacture easy, the body of the gun was made from heavy steel stampings welded and pinned together – this replaced the older system of machining gun bodies from solid steel, and made manufacture both cheaper and quicker. A wooden butt was fitted to the rear of the gun body, and a plastic fore-end, beneath the front of the gun body, gave the firer's second hand something to grasp when controlling the weapon.

Early success

The result, the UZI sub-machine gun, went into production in 1951. It was an immediate sucess and was soon standard issue throughout the Israeli army.

The UZI was rapidly taken into service by the Federal German Army, the Netherlands army, and the armies of Ireland, Belgium, Thailand and many other countries. It has also been widely used by police and security agencies throughout the world.

By the early 1980s smaller SMGs were all the rage, and the Israelis produced the Mini-UZI. This uses exactly the same mechanism but is reduced in all dimensions so that the gun, with stock folded, is only 360 mm long, with a 197 mm barrel. Instead of the folding stock, the Mini-UZI merely has a steel wire stock with shoulder-pad which folds sideways, the shoulder-pad acting as a forward handgrip. The whole gun, when empty, weighs only 2.7 kg, and a special short 20-round magazine is used instead of the

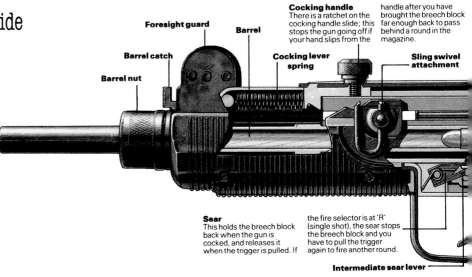

Foresight guard

Barrel catch

Barrel nut

Barrel

Cocking handle
There is a ratchet on the cocking handle slide; this stops the gun going off if your hand slips from the

handle after you have brought the breech block far enough back to pass behind a round in the magazine.

Cocking lever spring

Sling swivel attachment

Sear
This holds the breech block back when the gun is cocked, and releases it when the trigger is pulled. If

the fire selector is at 'R' (single shot), the sear stops the breech block and you have to pull the trigger again to fire another round.

Intermediate sear lever

Loading the UZI

Hold the weapon in your right hand in an upright position, pointing up at about 60°. Tilt the UZI to the right and insert the magazine with your left hand. Push it home until it snaps into place, and give the base of the magazine a slap with the palm of your left hand.

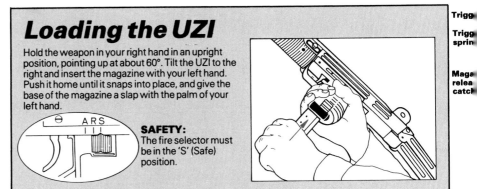

SAFETY:
The fire selector must be in the 'S' (Safe) position.

Trigg

Trigg sprin

Maga relea catch

Field stripping the UZI

In keeping with its simplicity, the UZI is an easy weapon to field strip. Only five parts need to be handled, and no tools are required. Strip the gun on a clean surface; in the field, use a jacket, for example. To make re-assembly easy, place each part on the jacket in the order it was removed. Re-assembly is done in reverse order.

1 Remove the top cover by depressing the catch, which is in the forward end of the rearsight seating.

2 Lift the rear part of the cover and pull it upwards and backwards to remove it from the gun.

4 Remove the breechblock and return spring assembly by bringing it forwards over the front sight.

5 Press the barrel catch in the front part of the foresight seating, and unscrew the barrel nut.

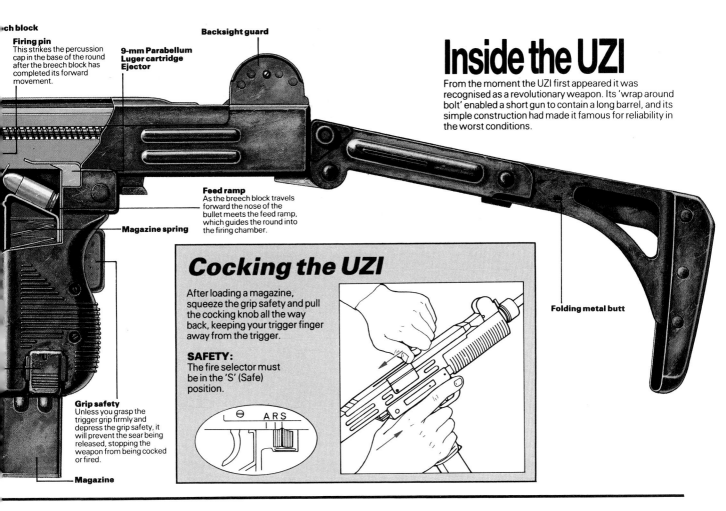

ch block

Firing pin
This strikes the percussion cap in the base of the round after the breech block has completed its forward movement.

9-mm Parabellum Luger cartridge Ejector

Backsight guard

Inside the UZI

From the moment the UZI first appeared it was recognised as a revolutionary weapon. Its 'wrap around bolt' enabled a short gun to contain a long barrel, and its simple construction had made it famous for reliability in the worst conditions.

Feed ramp
As the breech block travels forward the nose of the bullet meets the feed ramp, which guides the round into the firing chamber.

Magazine spring

Folding metal butt

Cocking the UZI

After loading a magazine, squeeze the grip safety and pull the cocking knob all the way back, keeping your trigger finger away from the trigger.

SAFETY:
The fire selector must be in the 'S' (Safe) position.

A R S

Grip safety
Unless you grasp the trigger grip firmly and depress the grip safety, it will prevent the sear being released, stopping the weapon from being cocked or fired.

Magazine

3 Raise the breechblock until its front is clear of the gun body.

6 Pulling the barrel out completes the basic field strip.

This UZI is field stripped and ready for basic maintenance. Most malfunctions in sub-machine guns are caused by negligence: failure to clean the working parts or spot barrel bulging or problems with the extractor. Before oiling, the bore must be so clean that you can pass a piece of white flannel along it without it getting dirty.

25-round or 32-round magazines of the original UZI design.

As if this were not enough, in 1985 the company produced the 'Micro-UZI'. This has been shrunk even more, to a length of only 250 mm with the wire stock folded, weighs 1.95 kg empty, and uses the same 20-round magazine as the Mini-UZI.

The technical drawback to small sub-machine guns is that as the size

'Son of UZI': intended for commando and security operations and just 36 cm long, the Mini-UZI is a scaled down version of the original. It is seen here fitted with a silencer, which also makes a useful hand grip.

Battlefield Evaluation: comparing

UZI

The UZI introduced the 'wrap around bolt', which enables a relatively short gun to house a barrel long enough to give reasonable accuracy at up to 200 metres. The magazine's position in the handgrip makes it much easier to change in the dark, and the grip safety prevents the gun going off if it is dropped after being cocked – a familiar problem with older SMGs such as the British Sten gun. The UZI is a first-class weapon for close-quarter fighting.

Specification:
Cartridge: 9-mm Parabellum
Weight: 4 kg
Length: (stock folded) 47 cm
Cyclic rate of fire: 600 rounds per minute
Magazine: 25-, 32- or 40-round box
Effective range: 200 m

Assessment
Reliability   ★★★★★
Accuracy   ★★★
Age   ★★★★★
Worldwide users   ★★★★

The UZI has established a remarkable reputation for reliability in combat conditions.

Beretta Model 12

The Beretta Model 12 is a popular weapon. After being adopted by the Italian army it was sold widely in North Africa, Latin America and the Far East. Like the UZI it uses a wrap-around bolt to reduce the overall length of the gun, but it is a more conventional design; the magazine housing is separate from the trigger grip. It is a reliable weapon and pleasingly accurate.

Specification:
Cartridge: 9-mm Parabellum
Weight: 3.8 kg
Length: (stock folded) 42 cm
Cyclic rate of fire: 550 rounds per minute
Magazine: 20-, 32- or 40-round box
Effective range: 200 m

Assessment
Reliability   ★★★★
Accuracy   ★★★★
Age   ★★★★
Worldwide users   ★★★

Rather bulkier but nevertheless accurate, the Beretta Model 12 is almost as widely used as the UZI.

Steyr MPi 69

The Steyr's rate of fire is controlled by trigger pressure. This takes some getting used to, and tends to mean that if you are confronted with a surprise target you fire a full burst. The cocking handle is attached to the sling, which allows you to cock the weapon by yanking on the sling rather than fumbling for the handle. This has led to some recruits accidentally firing guns they had inadvertently cocked, and the latest version of this gun, the MPi 81, has a normal cocking handle.

Specification:
Cartridge: 9-mm Parabellum
Weight: 3.5 kg
Length: (stock folded) 46.5 cm
Cyclic rate of fire: 550 rounds per minute
Magazine: 25 or 32-round box
Effective range: 200 m

Assessment
Reliability   ★★★
Accuracy   ★★★★
Age   ★★★
Worldwide users   ★

The Steyr MPi 69 and 81 fire either single shots or fully automatic, depending on trigger pressure.

goes down, so does the mass of the bolt. This is going to be blown back very much faster, is going to return faster, and the gun is thus going to have a very high rate of fire, making the weapon less easy to control. The original UZI fired at 600 rounds per minute; the Mini-UZI fires at 950 rounds per minute.

Weight increase

Something had to be done to the bolt of the Micro-UZI or it would be so fast as to be uncontrollable, so the designer placed a heavy tungsten insert into the bolt to beef up the weight, keeping the rate of fire down to a mere 1250 rounds per minute. This means that an incautious squeeze of the trigger can empty the magazine in 0.95 of a second!

New machine-guns have appeared with surprising frequency in the last 20 years, but the UZI family continues to hold its own. Its crude strength and reliability are proven, and where new weapons can point only to successful factory tests the UZI can boast over 30 years of success in combat.

The West German army was one of the first foreign armies to adopt the UZI. It is issued mainly as a personal weapon for tank and vehicle crews.

the UZI with its rivals

Heckler & Koch MP5

When the SAS stormed the Iranian Embassy in London in 1981, TV viewers in the UK saw the MP5 in action. Another version of this increasingly popular weapon equips the police units deployed to Gatwick, Heathrow and other British air terminals after the 1986 terrorist attacks on Rome and Vienna airports. The MP5 is a far more complex weapon than the UZI and a good deal more expensive, but it is probably the most accurate sub-machine gun in the world.

Specification:
Cartridge: 9-mm Parabellum
Weight: 3 kg
Length: (stock folded) 49 cm
Cyclic rate of fire: 800 rounds per minute
Magazine: 15- or 30- round box
Effective range: 200 m

Assessment
Reliability	★★★★★
Accuracy	★★★★★
Age	★★★
Worldwide users	★★★

The MP5 is a far more complicated weapon than the UZI, and is the most accurate SMG in service.

Sterling L2A3

This has been the standard sub-machine gun of the British Army since the early 1950s; the heavy weapons crew and other personnel currently issued with it will eventually receive SA80s with iron sights instead. A hefty weapon, the Sterling is reliable even in bad conditions, but it is basically an obsolete design. It does not use a wrap-around bolt, so although the Sterling is longer overall than the UZI its barrel is over 6 cm shorter.

Specification:
Cartridge: 9-mm Parabellum
Weight: 3.5 kg
Length: (stock folded) 48 cm
Cyclic rate of fire: 550 rounds per minute
Magazine: 34-round box
Effective range: 150 m

Assessment
Reliability	★★★★
Accuracy	★★★
Age	★★★★★
Worldwide users	★★★★

The Sterling may be obsolete, but it is machined to a very high standard and is a weapon you can depend on.

Spectre

This Italian sub-machine gun is a relatively new design that is beginning to make an impression. It has a unique 'double action' mechanism that allows you to carry the gun cocked, but safe, and to fire simply by pulling the trigger. Pulling the cocking handle and releasing it lets the bolt forward, chambering a round and closing the breech. Pulling the trigger cocks and releases a hammer like a double action revolver, which means you do not have to spend valuable moments cocking a gun if you are caught by surprise.

Specification:
Cartridge: 9-mm Parabellum
Weight: 3.8 kg
Length: (stock folded) 35 cm
Cyclic rate of fire: 900 rounds per minute
Magazine: 30 or 50-round box
Effective range: 150 m

Assessment
Reliability	★★★★
Accuracy	★★★★
Age	★
Worldwide users	★

The Spectre has a fearsome rate of fire and a 50-round magazine, making it a devastating close-range weapon.

INTO BATTLE WITH THE BRADLEY

Dawn in central Europe. Out of the darkness comes the clatter of tracks and the rumble of powerful engines: US M1 Main Battle Tanks and M2 Bradley Infantry Fighting Vehicles are on the prowl. Inside the Bradley, the driver sees clearly through his infra-red night-driving equipment. The gunner, sitting high up in the small turret, has an image intensifier to seek out targets for the 25-mm Chain Gun and twin TOW anti-tank guided missiles.

The M1 tanks exit the forest and deploy in staggered echelon formation. As they accelerate across the open ground, the Bradleys swing out to the flanks, presenting the enemy with interlocking fields of fire: a lethal combination of 120-mm tank guns, anti-tank missiles, and cannon. The Bradley complements the power of the Main Battle Tank by providing suppressive fire and dismounting its infantry squad to take out enemy anti-tank weapons.

Infantry support

The concept of the armoured personnel carrier is as old as that of the tank, and experience has shown that tanks need close support from their own infantry. This was repeatedly demonstrated in World War II and more recently in 1973 when Israeli tanks charged alone against Egyptian positions along the Suez canal – and were bloodily repulsed. All mechanised armies employed APCs as battlefield taxis to allow their infantry to manoeuvre on to the battlefield while still protected against shell splinters and small arms fire.

Building on their World War II experience, the Soviets went a step further. In the mid-1960s they introduced the BMP, a tracked APC fitted with a turret-mounted 73-mm low velocity gun and the AT-3 'Sagger' anti-tank guided missile. The infantry companies within Soviet armoured

You exit the Bradley through a large, hydraulically-operated ramp in the rear of the hull.

Seen here demonstrating its incredible speed cross-country, the Bradley is designed to fight in close conjunction with M1 Abrams Main Battle Tanks and is the most expensive and best-equipped vehicle of its kind.

divisions now rode into battle in the BMP and were trained to fight from the vehicle as well as dismounted. With its gun to provide supporting fire and engage enemy APCs and a missile system able to knock out Main Battle Tanks, the BMP gave Soviet infantry a tremendous advantage.

Outperforming the rest

The Bradley is designed to trump the BMP. Its McDonnell Douglas 25-mm Chain Gun fires APDS (Armour-Piercing Discarding Sabot) shells at up to 500 rounds per minute. It is accurate at up to 2,500 metres, and its twin TOW anti-tank guided missiles can knock out any tank currently in service at over 3,000 metres. Expressly designed for speed and manoeuvrability, the Bradley handles well and its cross-country ability is substantially superior to that of the old M113.

The Americans had first experimented with Infantry Fighting Vehicles in Vietnam, where they fitted extra machine-guns to M113 APCs (Armoured Cavalry Vehicles). The 'ACAVs' used fire-and-man-

The Bradley has one feature common to most Soviet Armoured Fighting Vehicles: it can generate a smoke screen by injecting diesel fuel into the exhaust. Unlike the British MCV-80 the Bradley is fully amphibious, propelling itself through the water with its tracks.

oeuvre tactics to defeat the Viet Cong. ACAV crews fought from the vehicle instead of plunging into the undergrowth; they responded to ambushes by accelerating and driving into the enemy positions, firing in all directions. Where the enemy were short of effective anti-tank weapons this proved devastatingly effective – the Viet Cong had no answer to aggressively-handled APCs with awesome firepower.

Rifle firing port

In addition to the turret-mounted hardware, each infantryman inside the Bradley has a firing port through which he can fire an M231 5.56-mm rifle, essentially a cut-down M16 with an extendable wire stock which is designed to be used from the cramped interior of a combat vehicle. With a cyclic rate of fire of between 1100 and 1300 rounds per minute, you can empty the 30-round magazine in under 1½ seconds! For this reason the Bradley carries 600 rounds per firing port weapon.

The US Army has ordered nearly

Infantry and Cavalry Fighting Vehicles

There are two versions of the Bradley: the M2, the basic Infantry Fighting Vehicle carrying a full squad of infantry, and the M3, a reconnaissance vehicle.

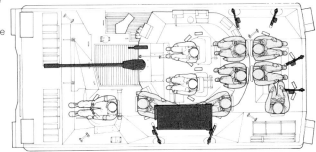

M2
The M2 carries seven infantrymen and the driver in its hull. The gunner sits in the left-hand side of the turret and the vehicle commander, who dismounts with the infantry, in the right-hand side. Six firing ports are provided so that the infantry can shoot from inside the vehicle.

M3
Looking identical from the outside, the M3 carries a crew of only five but nearly twice as much ammunition, including 15 TOW anti-tank missiles, 1,200 25-mm cannon shells, and 4,500 7.62-mm bullets.

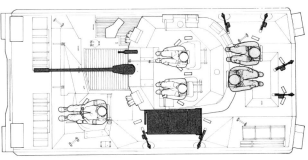

The troop compartment of the Bradley is very cramped, but not such a tight squeeze as in the Soviet BMP series IFVs. The Bradley has to be able to keep pace with the gas turbine-powered M1 tanks, but high-speed cross-country driving is very exhausting.

the levels expected, and all hatches, including the heavy rear ramp, were consequently blown out.

It was claimed that in the initial tests, shots were deliberately aimed away from vulnerable fuel and ammunition storage areas and that the dummies inside representing the crew members were soaked in water to stop their clothes catching fire. The Bradley has been fitted with an inert gas fire suppression system but the gas they used, Halon, reacted with a

7,000 Bradleys. The first Bradleys entered service in 1983 and some 2,000 have now been delivered.

However, as the Bradley programme gathered pace, many criticisms have emerged. It has been claimed that the Bradley's armour was not even proof against Soviet machine-guns firing their new armour-piercing ammunition; that the Bradley was a step backwards from the M113, which carried a bigger infantry squad; and that it was incapable of keeping up with the gas turbine-powered M1 Abrams MBT. As for the opposition, the Soviets have already updated the BMP by adding a new turret carrying a fully-stabilised 30-mm cannon and an AT-5 'Spandrel' anti-tank missile-launcher. A special mount allows the 'Spandrel' missiles to be fired outside the vehicle.

Computer-tested

Under questioning, it was admitted that most of the tests that proved the Bradley could withstand hits from anti-tank weapons were computer simulations, not live firing tests. The US Army promptly organised a series of live firing tests to examine the performance of the Bradley's defensive systems, only for critics to claim these tests were rigged.

The Bradley was tested in two phases: Phase 1 against current Soviet weapons known to be in service, and Phase 2 against projected weapons with an improved performance.

Fudges and fixes

The critics of the first tests cited a damning series of fudges and fixes used to pass the Bradley. Romanian-manufactured RPG-7 anti-tank rockets were fired from 18 metres, which is so close that the rocket does not have time to reach full velocity. TOW anti-tank missiles were exploded statically, and when one was detonated at a 25° angle at the insistence of an Air Force Colonel overseeing the test, the result was catastrophic. Pressure and temperature effects were double

Inside the Bradley

The M2 Bradley Infantry Fighting Vehicle is protected by all-welded aluminium armour with spaced laminate armour fitted to the hull, sides and rear. Its tremendous armament gives it the edge over any rival IFV, but doubts remain about its ability to survive a hit from a large-calibre weapon.

Turret
Part steel and part aluminium armoured, the turret has 360° traverse, moving at 60° per second, and can elevate the cannon and machine-gun to +60. The turret drive and stabilisation system allows the cannon to be accurately aimed and fired even when the vehicle is moving.

7.62-mm M240C co-axial machine-gun
This has 800 rounds at the ready and another 1,540 in reserve. It is mainly for anti-personnel use

McDonnell Douglas Helicopter Company M242 25-mm Chain Gun
The gunner sets the cannon to fire at either 100, 200 or 500 rounds per minute. All moving parts are operated by a single double-row roller chain which cycles in a racetrack pattern. Spent cases are ejected forward, out of the turret, and a dual feed system allows the gunner to switch ammunition type.

M257 Smoke Discharger
Electrically operated, the M257 fires a pattern of four smoke grenades in front of the Bradley as an emergency defence measure.

Engine compartment
The Cummins VTA-903T turbo-charged 8-cylinder diesel engine develops 500 hp at 2600 rpm. It is equipped with a Halon (inert gas) fire suppression system.

fuel fire to produce toxic fumes. Not quite the intended result.

The M2 Bradley carries 900 25-mm cannon shells; 2,340 7.62-mm bullets; 4,200 5.56-mm bullets; and 10 TOW anti-tank missiles. The M3 carries substantially more of everything. Add 662 litres of fuel, and you can see why the US Congressional Report concluded that enemy shots would probably hit something vital and "catastrophic explosions are likely to occur with unacceptable frequency during combat".

Congress forced the Pentagon to conduct operational and live fire tests on two modified versions of the Bradley. The tests did show the Bradley to be proof against small-arms fire, from 7.62-mm bullets up to the 14.5-mm ammunition used by Soviet heavy machine-guns. It was also proof against 155-mm shell fragments from overhead bursts, but it seems the Bradley is still vulnerable to shaped-charge infantry anti-tank weapons.

The solution may be the application of reactive armour. Tested by the

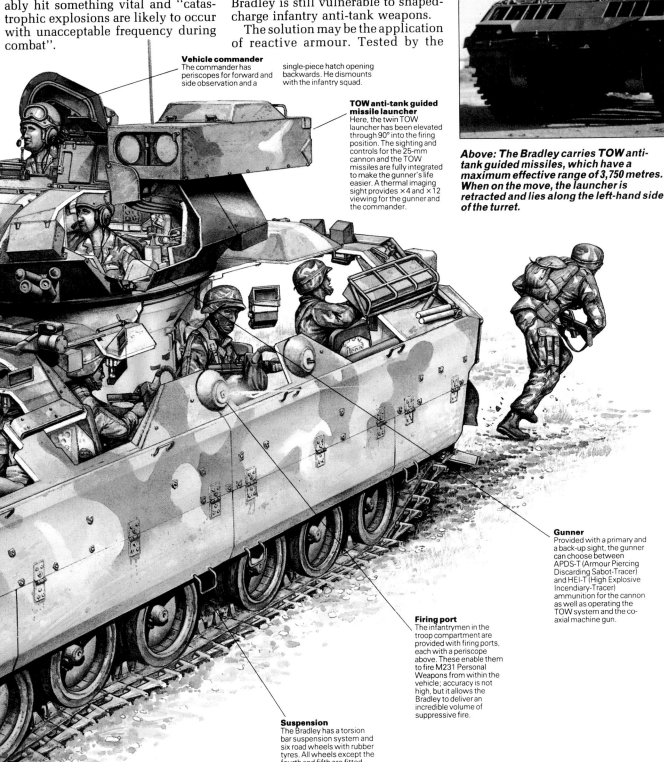

Above: The Bradley carries TOW anti-tank guided missiles, which have a maximum effective range of 3,750 metres. When on the move, the launcher is retracted and lies along the left-hand side of the turret.

Vehicle commander
The commander has periscopes for forward and side observation and a single-piece hatch opening backwards. He dismounts with the infantry squad.

TOW anti-tank guided missile launcher
Here, the twin TOW launcher has been elevated through 90° into the firing position. The sighting and controls for the 25-mm cannon and the TOW missiles are fully integrated to make the gunner's life easier. A thermal imaging sight provides ×4 and ×12 viewing for the gunner and the commander.

Gunner
Provided with a primary and a back-up sight, the gunner can choose between APDS-T (Armour Piercing Discarding Sabot-Tracer) and HEI-T (High Explosive Incendiary-Tracer) ammunition for the cannon as well as operating the TOW system and the co-axial machine gun.

Firing port
The infantrymen in the troop compartment are provided with firing ports, each with a periscope above. These enable them to fire M231 Personal Weapons from within the vehicle; accuracy is not high, but it allows the Bradley to deliver an incredible volume of suppressive fire.

Suspension
The Bradley has a torsion bar suspension system and six road wheels with rubber tyres. All wheels except the fourth and fifth are fitted with hydraulic shock absorbers.

Israelis in Lebanon, this consists of panels of explosive which are detonated by the impact of a large enemy projectile. The resulting explosion dissipates the 'blowtorch' blast of a hollow-charge warhead and saves the vehicle.

Bradleys are now entering production with revised internal arrangements, different fuel and fire suppression systems and new NBC protection. The Army's plans for future upgrading include thermal image de-

It takes a well-trained crew about 15 minutes to erect the Special Water Barrier that enables the Bradley to operate amphibiously.

Battlefield Evaluation: comparing

M2 Bradley Infantry Fighting Vehicle

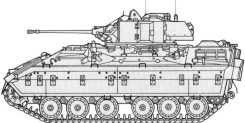

Replacing the M113 APCs in the mechanised infantry battalions but not in all other roles, the M2 Bradley is now the subject of a classified programme of modifications which is intended to dramatically improve its capabilities. For the time being, the Bradley remains an expensive vehicle of questionable cost-effectiveness. Each series of tests seems to have posed more questions than it answered.

Specification:
Combat weight: 22.5 tonnes
Maximum road speed: 66 km/h
Power to weight ratio: 20 hp/tonne
Length: 6.45 m
Height: 2.97 m
Crew: 3+7
Armament: 25-mm cannon; 7.62-mm MG; TOW; 5.56-mm port guns

Assessment
Firepower	★★★★★
Protection	★★★
Age	★
Worldwide users	★

The Bradley is heavily armed, but doubts remain about its survivability.

MCV-80 Warrior Infantry Fighting Vehicle

The Warrior is the British equivalent of the Bradley, and the first production vehicles were being completed in December 1986 ready for delivery. The Warrior is armed with the tried-and-tested RARDEN 30-mm cannon and a 7.62-mm Chain Gun. Although heavier than the Bradley it is faster. However, Warrior is not amphibious and the infantrymen cannot fire their personal weapons from inside.

Specification:
Combat weight: 24.5 tonnes
Maximum road speed: 75 km/h
Power to weight ratio: 22.5 hp/tonne
Length: 6.34 m
Height: 2.73 m
Crew: 3+7
Armament: 30-mm cannon and 7.62-mm Chain Gun

Assessment
Firepower	★★★★★
Protection	★★★
Age	★
Worldwide users	★

Warrior is due to enter service with the British Army during 1987.

AMX-10

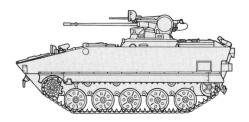

The AMX-10 entered service with the French army in 1973, and with typical energy the French have sold it widely in the Middle East, Saudi Arabia alone buying 300 vehicles. The two-man turret is slightly off centre, and mounts a 20-mm cannon with a maximum range of about 1500 metres; a dual-feed system allows the gunner to select either High Explosive or Armour Piercing ammunition. There are a large number of AMX-10 variants, including a special model designed for amphibious operations sold to the Indonesian Marines.

Specification:
Combat weight: 14.5 tonnes
Maximum road speed: 65 km/h
Power to weight ratio: 20 hp/tonne
Length: 5.78 m
Height: 2.57 m
Crew: 3+8
Armament: 1 × 20-mm cannon; 1 × 7.62-mm MG

Assessment
Firepower	★★
Protection	★★★
Age	★★★
Worldwide users	★★★

The AMX-10 is the IFV member of a large family of armoured fighting vehicles.

vices, low-profile radio antennas, improved fault-finding systems and a new 35-mm cannon.

The US Army cannot afford to have doubts about the Bradley, if not for the congressmen then for the sake of the soldiers who may find out the hard way whether the Bradley measures up to the modern battlefield. Sources close to the Pentagon confirm that the US Army is planning further changes to the Bradley which will alter it out of all recognition. The exact details remain classified, and in the meantime the Army continues to take deliveries of the world's most expensive Infantry Fighting Vehicle.

MILES on the M2

The US Army makes extensive use of battlefield simulators; this is a MILES laser transmitter fitted above the Bradley's 25-mm cannon. MILES (Multiple Integrated Laser Engagement System) uses eye-safe laser beams to simulate the firing of live ammunition. Men and vehicles taking part in a tactical exercise are fitted with detectors that signal a hit or near miss. This system allows for realistic training in battle tactics, and can be fitted on all direct-fire weapons, from rifles to tank guns and attack helicopters.

the Bradley with its rivals

BMP-2

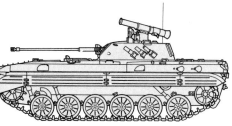

The BMP-1 was the first purpose-built Infantry Fighting Vehicle, and it startled Western observers when it was first identified in 1967. Widely used in the Arab-Israeli wars of 1973 and 1982, Afghanistan and the Gulf War, it has now been substantially improved. The 73-mm smooth-bore gun has been replaced by a far more effective 30-mm cannon plus the AT-5 'Spandrel' anti-tank guided missile. The BMP is fully amphibious and has NBC protection.

Specification:
Combat weight: 14.6 tonnes
Maximum road speed: 65 km/h
Power to weight ratio: undisclosed
Length: 6.71 m
Height: 2 m
Crew: 3+7
Armament: 1 × 30-mm cannon; 1 × 7.6-mm MG; 1 launcher for AT-5 'Spandrel' missile

Assessment
Firepower	****
Protection	***
Age	*
Worldwide users	***

The BMP-2 is a much-improved version of the original BMP.

M113 Armoured Personnel Carrier

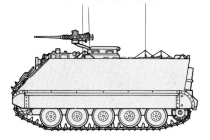

The M113 is still in production and in service with over 50 different armies. Typical of the APCs developed in the 1950s, it was originally a very simple, bullet-proof armoured box on tracks armed with a single machine-gun. M113s have been converted into a bewildering variety of vehicles, ranging from field modifications carried out in Vietnam and Israel to the current US Army improvement programme planned for its whole fleet of about 18,000 M113s.

Specification:
(M113A1)
Combat weight: 11 tonnes
Maximum road speed: 67 km/h
Power to weight ratio: 19 hp/tonne
Length: 4.86 m
Height: 2.5 m
Crew: 2+11
Armament: 1 × Browning 0.50-cal machine-gun

Assessment
Firepower	*
Protection	**
Age	*****
Worldwide users	*****

The M113 was used in vast numbers during the Vietnam War.

Marder

The Marder is a very large but powerful Infantry Fighting Vehicle. In the 1950s the Germans developed a chassis which was intended to serve as the basis for a whole range of military vehicles. Most of the range never left the drawing board, but despite its large size for an IFV the Marder was adopted by the West German army in 1968. The turret armament is supplemented by a remote-controlled 7.62-mm machine-gun above the troop compartment.

Specification:
Combat weight: 29 tonnes
Maximum road speed: 75 km/h
Power to weight ratio: 20.5 hp/tonne
Length: 6.79 m
Height: 2.98 m
Crew: 4+6
Armament: 1 × 20-mm cannon; 1 × co-axial 7.62-mm MG; 1 × remote-controlled 7.62-mm MG

Assessment
Firepower	***
Protection	***
Age	***
Worldwide users	*

The West German army's Marders are the biggest and heaviest IFVs in service.

Survival
Hijack!
Part 1

Stay loose
Travel in loose, comfortable clothing: if you are hijacked you'll have to keep cool, clean and healthy for some time. Play mind games to keep yourself sane.

The family man
If kept in close quarters with a hijacker, talk about your own and his family. Make yourself a real, normal person in his eyes and you'll be treated better. Don't talk politics.

Non-provocative kit
Don't wear religious or other insignia: the hijackers may not share your beliefs. And no provocative T-shirts with political slogans either!

Sick leave
If you can feign symptoms of sickness and keep it up, you may be released in an interim deal.

Decompression
Most modern handguns will penetrate the fuselage of an airliner, which would result in catastrophic loss of pressurisation. To a fanatical or nervous hijacker this may not count for much, but it could bring down the aircraft and kill everyone on board.

You switch on the 6 o'clock news and once again you see an airliner parked at the end of a runway. It shimmers in the heat reflected from the concrete and you can see armoured cars and troops lurking by the control tower. The terrorists' demands seem wearily familiar, and there's no comment yet from the White House. But hijacks don't just happen to other people. One day it might be you.

You can survive some hijacks, like some ambushes, by careful planning and thinking ahead. Don't just follow the crowd: think through your schedule, the different routes to your destination and the airlines you might fly with.

The very first priority is to establish if you, or anyone you might be with, is a potential target. Remember that you are more likely to be singled out because of what you represent than who you actually are: terrorists often attack people just because of their nationality. If they simply want British hos-

tages, you might fit the bill very nicely just because you happen to be in the wrong place at the wrong time.

The second area of prior planning is the booking, route, carrier and seat. Make two bookings on different airlines, but only pick up one. Collect these tickets at the airport, so that your movements are known to a limited number of people. Choose an airline like Swissair or SAS which has no political associations. Some of the US carriers are obvious targets, as are Middle East airlines. Go for the neutrals – even countries with former colonial empires can be targets.

Avoid stopovers

Try and make sure that you have a direct route with no stop-overs – this is particularly important with the Middle East. Some airports have very sloppy security, and while you may have had a thorough search when you boarded at your departure, other passengers at other stops may board less thoroughly checked.

If there is a stop-over, a walk around the terminal will get you away from the vulnerable aircraft – some terrorists have boarded aircraft disguised as cleaners during stop-overs, so a stroll reduces your chances of being caught in the hijack.

If you are flying to a potential trouble spot some airlines are noted for their high level of security – El Al insists on searches of baggage as well as electronic and body checks of passengers. They are also one of the many airlines that now operates with 'sky marshals'. El Al may be a target, but it is a 'hard' target.

Your seat could be a lifesaver – aisle

seats put you within reach of the hijacker. Window seats are safer, and exit seats may give you the chance to escape if the aircraft is on the runway of an airport.

Stay in tourist class

'Neutral' seating in tourist class is less likely to attract attention than first class. If the terrorists wish to show their determination they may shoot hostages, and these are likely to have been chosen from passengers who are obviously important.

Your dress and manner will also make you a target. In some countries blue jeans are seen as Western clo-

An American airliner hijacked by Shi'ite Muslim terrorists taxis along the runway at Beirut airport. The gunmen demanded the release of Arabs held in Israel.

The most dangerous situation is a group with automatic weapons and explosives. The explosives may be positioned around the aircraft, with the threat that they will be detonated if there is an attempt at rescue; and automatic weapons are notoriously inaccurate in untrained hands, and could cause casualties if a firefight with a sky marshal developed.

If there is a firefight, stay as low as possible. Window seats give better cover, though they are less easy to escape from. The sky marshal will probably have a low-velocity weapon with ammunition that will not damage the fuselage, but the hijacker may be using a 9 mm high-velocity weapon – and if this punctures the aircraft fuselage there may be decompression.

Rash rescue attempts

However, the aim of the hijacker is to get the plane to a place where the bargaining can begin. There have recently been examples where hastily-mounted 'rescue' operations have caused more casualties than were expected when the rescuers stormed the aircraft. If a rescue operation takes

Terrorists in action: a British and a Swiss airliner burn on a Jordanian airstrip after Palestinian gunmen dynamited them. In this case the passengers were removed from the plane first but other hostages have not been so lucky.

thing, and so are suspect. Ex-army clothing is to be avoided, combat jackets being the most obvious. Baggage also draws attention either by its opulence or by being service issue, for example kit bags or rucksacks.

Labels should only have a business address, and the baggage should not sport hotel labels from around the world (incidentally, these precautions also reduce the chance of theft at airports). Jewellery, striking T-shirts and obvious ethnic clothing can also be a liability and reduce your ability to be the 'grey man', a neutral unnoticed in the passengers.

Keep your passport clean

Finally, your passport and wallet can contain a goldmine of information. Try to avoid collecting visa stamps from countries that have a terrorist problem – many countries will stamp entry and exit visas on a separate piece of paper if you ask.

Your job description can be a major liability – government or service personnel are seen as 'targets' by many hijackers and natural targets for hostage executions.

Photographs of relatives and children are always worth including in your wallet/passport. You will be seen as a family man or woman with dependents and thus a less suitable person for execution. At the other extreme, the bathing-costume picture of a wife or girlfriend may cast you as a corrupt and decadent Westerner in the eyes of some hijackers.

Action

If the worst happens and you are on the aircraft that has been hijacked, follow the old army adage: 'Keep your eyes open, your mouth shut and never volunteer for anything'. The last part

For 16 days the crew of the TWA flight hijacked to Beirut were held in the cabin of their aircraft. The other passengers were dispersed throughout the Muslim-held suburbs.

can be modified if it allows you to escape.

As the hijack is taking place the armed men and women will be very nervous, and rapid or unexpected movements from the passengers may produce violent reactions They may assault you, note you as a future execution victim, or kill you as a suspected sky marshal.

By quiet observation you will be able to build up a picture of the numbers of hijackers and their mode of operation. In a big aircraft they may collect everyone together, or position themselves at different points around it to cover the passengers.

Tiredness and tension

As time passes everyone will be affected by fatigue and the need to perform bodily functions. This will increase tension, and the presence of children will further aggravate this.

The hijackers will probably release women, children and elderly people if the aircraft has landed at a location where negotiations are taking place. These released passengers will be able to give details of the hijackers to the security forces, assuming that the aircraft is in a reasonably pro-Western country.

If you have a seat by the door there may be an opportunity to escape. However, if you are travelling with a group this may make them potential execution victims. Note how the hijacker is armed – if he has a hand gun you have a better chance of surviving, and there may even be a chance to overwhelm him.

place, the most likely course of action will be for the assault team to order the passengers to keep down. In this way they can identify the hijackers, who are likely to be on their feet in the aisle.

Your best course is to keep down and wait for the shooting to stop; the assault team will be looking for any violent or unexpected movement. They will have preceded the assault with stun grenades, and both passengers and hijackers will be suffering from temporary shock. The team will then aim to have the passengers off the aircraft as fast as possible, so you should follow their instructions.

Keep cool

If, however, the aircraft arrives at a neutral or 'friendly' country where the hijackers can negotiate, the advisable course is to assess the situation. There may be friends of the hostages at the airport who will take over the negotiations with a foreign power and be more rational than the men and women who hijacked the aircraft. In this situation, a leader for the passengers may emerge; he could be the pilot or a mature and experienced passenger. Such a man will be able to make representations about the health and welfare of the passengers.

By this stage the aircraft and passengers will have become bargaining counters and their safety will be more important. Now it may be a time for patient waiting. If you find you are moved from the aircraft to hotels or holding areas, try to take some hand luggage or toiletries – there may be nothing when you arrive. Staying clean and presentable will also sustain your morale.

The inflight comforts will stop almost at once if a hijacking happens, since the stewardesses and stewards will be seen as conduits for information as they move around the aircraft. It is advisable therefore to keep hand luggage that contains simple toiletries

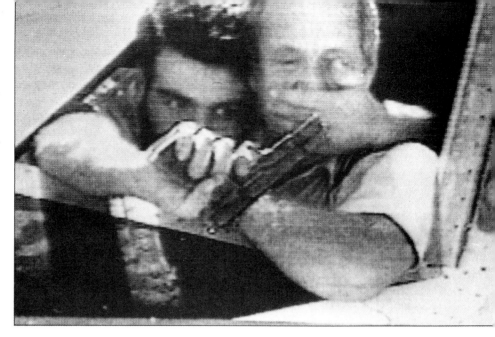

TWA pilot John Testrake is held at gun point by one of the hijackers. Using his knowledge of the aircraft the pilot can try to frustrate terrorist plans but this places him in great danger.

and any medication you may need ready to hand.

For many people hijacks, like other man-made or natural disasters, are experiences that happen to other people and which are reported on the news. But they could happen to almost anyone, even if they see themselves as 'Mr Average': they may be on the flight with an important traveller, or they may just be unlucky.

Survival

Hijack!

Part 2

Ever since the series of 'sky-jacks' in the late 1960s, anti-terrorist units have been refining a series of methods for storming a plane on the ground. It is no easy task. The terrorists have every advantage in their favour; they usually have a clear field of view and can slaughter the passengers in a matter of moments. If you are going to make a rescue attempt it must be planned to the last detail and executed with split-second timing.

Intelligence and planning

In some instances hijackers have released men and women who are sick or very young or old. These people will be vital since they will give information on the hijackers' numbers and their weapons and equipment. They will also provide more information on their level of training and motivation, though some of this will have been gleaned from the conversations with the control tower.

Wear them down

You will need to know how close you can approach without alerting the hijackers. Disguise as ground crew is a good cover, though ladders and weapons and equipment can be difficult to conceal. Night is the obvious time when the hijackers will be fatigued and there is reasonable cover.

If the APU (Auxiliary Power Unit) cuts out through lack of fuel, the internal lights, air conditioning and other power will cease, putting the aircraft in darkness. If the ground crew from the previous stop-over can advise on fuel states and it seems that there might be a breakdown, then an attack can be planned or the hijackers warned that the aircraft will be without power due to failure of the APU. Timing must be perfect: it was a failure to co-ordinate an APU breakdown that caused heavy casualties at Malta airport when Egyptian special forces attacked an airliner that had been hijacked.

Talking them out

The negotiating team can induce fatigue in the hijackers if they can keep them talking, although this must be balanced against the risk to the passengers, as well as their continuing discomfort. Sometimes the negotiators will be able to talk the hijackers out of the aircraft with no need to assault it, and no loss of life.

Losing patience

However, once hijackers lose patience with the negotiating team and start killing hostages to show that they mean business, then the assault team

must be ready to move in fast.

Since the hijackers are not likely to have weapons with rifle-calibre ammunition, your team could wear body armour, which will provide sufficient protection: the new lighter-weight Kevlar armour can be worn without reducing efficiency. The use of body armour is also important for the morale of the assault team.

Weapons for the assault team

The weapons for the job can include a linear cutting tape charge, stun grenades and automatics. Linear cutting tape is a flexible metal or plastic tube with a notch running along one face, and, correctly positioned, acts as a charge to cut through an aircraft fusel-

Dramatic events unfold aboard an Airbus hijacked and held at Tehran for six days, during which time two American passengers were shot. The long drawn-out negotiations are important: any assault will require time to plan, equip and rehearse.

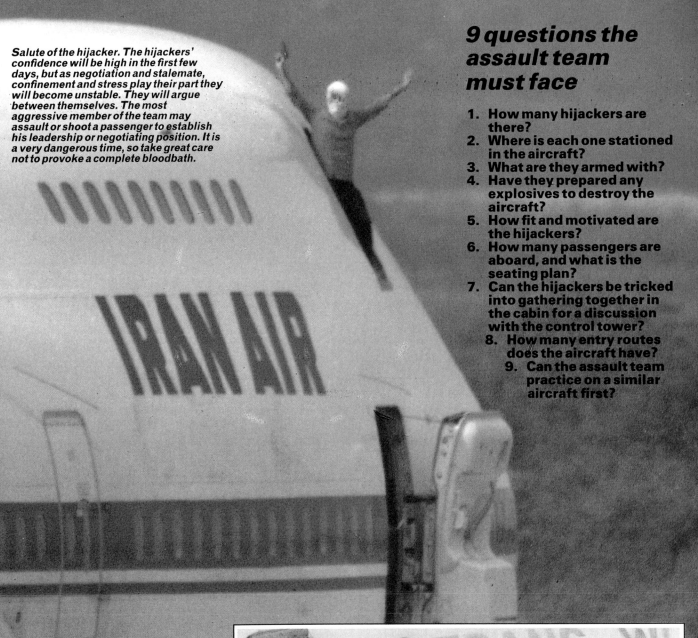

Salute of the hijacker. The hijackers' confidence will be high in the first few days, but as negotiation and stalemate, confinement and stress play their part they will become unstable. They will argue between themselves. The most aggressive member of the team may assault or shoot a passenger to establish his leadership or negotiating position. It is a very dangerous time, so take great care not to provoke a complete bloodbath.

9 questions the assault team must face

1. How many hijackers are there?
2. Where is each one stationed in the aircraft?
3. What are they armed with?
4. Have they prepared any explosives to destroy the aircraft?
5. How fit and motivated are the hijackers?
6. How many passengers are aboard, and what is the seating plan?
7. Can the hijackers be tricked into gathering together in the cabin for a discussion with the control tower?
8. How many entry routes does the aircraft have?
9. Can the assault team practice on a similar aircraft first?

age to gain entry. It can be fixed magnetically or with adhesives, according to the target.

Weapons for the firefight

The hand guns favoured by anti-hijack teams vary. The Delta Force in the USA originally used the venerable .45 M1919A1: the big slug will knock a man down without penetrating the aircraft fuselage. Hollow-point ammunition that flattens when it hits a target has a devastating effect on soft tissue, but will not ricochet or cause damage to internal controls and fittings in the aircraft.

New ammunition

Some new plastic ammunition will slow down after a short range, but is

Ground crew or Intelligence? The aircraft will need all sorts of services, and almost certainly Special Forces will be among the crews. Do not draw attention to anything unusual you see going on.

51

lethal over the short distances in which the action will take place. Automatics with large-capacity magazines like the Browning High Power, will give enough ammunition for the short but violent action that will follow the entry into the aircraft. However, you should carry spare magazines where they can be quickly loaded if there is a sustained firefight.

Entering the aircraft

If the hijackers are divided, with some on the flight deck and others amongst the passengers, then you will need to attack in two teams and stage the assault so that one team fights towards the front and one towards the back of the aircraft. This way, you should avoid firing into your own men. Entry must be preceded by stun grenades, which will temporarily disable the enemy but not severely injure the passengers.

Stun grenade effects

When a stun grenade explodes in a confined space like an airliner, anyone standing nearby will be completely deafened and if you are very close your eardrums will be shattered. The flash leaves you temporarily blinded, and if you were looking towards it when it went off the image will be burned onto your retina for at least 10 minutes, making it very hard for you to shoot straight.

Speed means success

However the rehearsals went, you must be ready for anything when you get inside the aircraft. The hijackers may not be where you expect them, and it's tempting to fight your way forward cautiously. But your attack will only succeed through speed/the volley of stun grenades and the suddenness of your assault throws the hijackers off balance, and you must not

The tense scene at Luqa airport, Malta, as Egyptian forces assault an airliner. Inside the plane, carnage is taking place. The hijackers are grenading their captives and the assault forces are firing indiscriminately.

give them time to recover.

Shout at the passengers to lie down. This will keep them out of the line of fire and should make the hijackers better targets. As you move through the smoke-filled aircraft hunting a handful of terrorists amongst hundreds of passengers, it is horribly easy to shoot the wrong target.

Standing targets

This is the moment all your training is for, when life or death hangs on your split-second reactions. If Intelligence managed to provide you with photos of the terrorists, at least you have some means of identifying your target, if not, then you must sweep through going for anyone standing or armed.

The passengers can be removed from the aircraft as soon as the hi-

Storming the aircraft

Surprise is the key to a successful attack on a hijacked airliner: the assault team must get on board and secure the aircraft in a matter of seconds. The security forces must deal with the terrorists immediately or they will begin massacring the passengers.

Non-provocative stance
Do not pick up weapons as you flee the aircraft – you may be shot as a suspected terrorist when you get outside. As you exit, fall to the floor as though injured with your arms outstretched, and stay there until instructed to move by security forces.

Cutting charge
One of the best ways to get inside the aircraft is to use a linear cutting charge – a flexible tube with a notch along one side that acts as a charge to cut through the fuselage.

Body armour
The number three man in the assault team must be particularly protected by body armour because he's the one likely to take rounds from the defending terrorists.

jackers are cleared from a major exit. Station members of your team by the exits to make sure no hijackers try to sneak out the same way and to co-ordinate the security forces outside the aircraft. There have been cases when escaping passengers were shot by mistake as they fled from the fighting.

Assault team moves out

After the hijackers have been dealt with and the aircraft declared 'clear', the assault team moves out. It is sensible to keep a low profile, because you do not want your arrival during a future crisis to be observed by the press and blasted all over the TV and radio. This is why all special forces preserve the anonymity of their men. It may save their lives one day – and it may save yours.

Aftermath of the chaos: Egyptian anti-terrorist forces pick over the survivors and corpses after their bungled assault. At least 50 passengers were killed by a mix of hijackers' and assault forces' weapons.

Obey all orders from the assault team without question or protest. They'll treat everyone as potential threats so you'll be handled very roughly until positively cleared.

Movement
Fighting in the confined interior of the aircraft, it is important to wear clothing that has no external fittings that could catch or snag.

Watch for grenades
As you sweep through the aircraft, anyone with a gun in their hand is an obvious target, but do not ignore the danger from grenades. An apparently unarmed passenger started rolling grenades along the aisle when the German GSG9 anti-terrorist team stormed an airliner at Mogadishu.

Soft-nosed ammunition
If you use hollow point or soft-nosed bullets, any rounds that miss their target will not richochet around the aircraft. Their other advantage is obvious: no hijacker hit by an expanding bullet is going to be in any condition to carry on fighting.

Tear gas will probably be used, so bury your head in the seat cushions. Do not rub your eyes – especially if you wear contact lenses.

Distraction
At the moment of assault there will be many distracting bangs and flashes. Most will be diversionary – the actual assault might come from anywhere.

Flash and stun grenades will be used immediately entry is made. They will cause temporary blindness, blow out nearby eardrums and cause confusion and panic.

Keep low
As soon as the action starts, slide to the floor under your seat and stay there. Do not move into the aisles; any assaulting troops will flatten you in their rush to dominate the aircraft.

ALL THE WAY

The helicopter seems to be dancing aimlessly over the countryside, skipping from place to place. But this aimless cruising is something much more deadly. For in the body of the helo squats a team of US Army Rangers, ready to set out on a long-range reconnaissance patrol in country that is at least as much enemy as it is friendly. And the purpose of their little dance around the countryside? Simple. Everywhere the aircraft touches down will be hidden from enemy watchers. Somewhere along the line its cargo of hard-bitten troopers will have de-planed and disappeared without a trace into the bush. But where?

Every army needs troops specially trained for the gruelling task of operating deep inside enemy-held territory. In the United States Army that position is held – and held proudly – by the Rangers. Their units go by many names, and vary in strength from a squad to an entire battalion, but no matter what they may be called, their objective is always the same – take the war to the enemy, and hit him before he even knows he's vulnerable.

Ranger origins

There are quite a few regiments that were raised as part of one nation's armed forces and now serve another, and the Rangers are one of them.

First raised in 1756 by Major Robert Rogers, a man of New Hampshire, the men of Roger's Rangers fought alongside the British in their wars against the French and the Indians. Then, as

The US Army Ranger school is open to all Army personnel who can pass a basic fitness test. The Army, Reserves, National Guard and ROTC all send men to the course, which is primarily an intensive patrolling course. Most of the successful students return to their units, but those who acquire a taste for the rigorous Ranger life can try for a place in 1/75 or 2/76 Rangers. Although the US Navy no longer sends personnel to the Ranger course (it has its own unit, the SEALs) the Ranger course is open to US Marines and men from America's allies.

The Ranger course lasts 58 gruelling days and has two main functions. First, you are taught how to lead a small unit behind enemy lines. You are working all the time and will be red-eyed with fatigue for the whole course: the lack of sleep is a problem which gets worse and worse as the course progresses. It is not unknown for otherwise excellent soldiers to give up the course only a few days from the end. In addition to the leadership training, the Ranger course teaches long-range patrolling. You have to think tactically the whole time, patrolling in all weathers and in all terrain.

now, their job was long-range patrolling.

Today's Rangers came into being on 19 June 1942 in the town of Carrickfergus, in Northern Ireland, when Major William O. Darby activated the 1st Ranger Battalion. These Rangers were all volunteers, mostly drawn from the 1st Armoured and 34th Infantry Divisions. They fought alongside British and Canadian Commandos in raids on the coast of Europe when Britain was the Allies' only foothold, and then saw action in every theatre of World War II.

Regular army

While the Rangers would be ranked amongst the élite of any army, they are not a 'Special' force such as Delta Force or the British SAS. They are firmly established as a part of the regular US Army, living and working alongside their colleagues in other infantry units.

Training is open to men from any branch of the US Armed Services, including Reserves, National Guard units and even ROTCs. Some candidates come from the Marine Corps, some from the Air Force and some from foreign allies. The Navy stopped sending men when it formed the SEAL units and worked up a training programme of its own.

Left: Rangers are not special forces: they are simply very well-trained infantrymen. Here a Ranger demonstrates their sniper gear, although he is armed with the standard M16 rather than a dedicated sniper rifle.

Left: Patrolling is at the heart of the Ranger training programme. You have only one hour of sleep in 24 and at any time the instructor can put you in command of planning and leading a patrol. It is a mind-numbing experience.

Right: Getting into the queue at the mess hall is a little tougher for a Ranger. You have to do a set number of chin-ups and go over the bar, not underneath it.

US Army Rangers take part in a recent exercise with the British 5 Airborne Brigade in Northumberland. Note the 'Fritz' helmets and M16A2 rifles, which fire three-round bursts rather than full auto. Tiger stripe face camouflage seemed particularly popular with the Rangers, who carried vast quantities of ammunition but no sleeping bags.

Fighting Fit

The 58 days of the Ranger School may sound short when you're on the outside looking in, but when you're up to your ass in it, 18 hours and more a day, it looks a little different.

And it is different from other infantry training programmes, chiefly because the men undergoing it are already some of the cream of their profession, trained soldiers who already have field experience. There are no badges of rank in evidence on a Ranger training course, and no preferential treatment for officers. It really bugs some of them, but they soon learn it's more important to be a strong member of a strong team than to sit on the false dignity of a bar on your collar.

Another factor that affects the way trainees go about learning the new set of skills is unit identification. Ranger training is not designed for individuals, but for groups of men who already know how to work together.

Above: Physical training is remorseless during the Ranger training – as are the barber's scissors. In the Ranger battalion you get your hair cut 'high and tight' every Sunday, ready for parade on Monday. Ranger regulations also ban moustaches and offensive T-shirts.

Below: 'H' Company, 75th Rangers in action near Xuan Loc, South Vietnam during 1970. Experience in South East Asia demonstrated the vital importance of the infantry skills taught to Rangers. There is no technological substitute for good infantry work.

Standing orders, Roger's Rangers
Major Robert Rogers, 1756

These instructions, written by the founder of the original Rangers, are as valid today as they were over 200 years ago. Major Rogers came from New Hampshire and organised nine companies of men to fight the French and their Indian allies during the Seven Years' War. His unit specialised in patrolling, and pioneered modern reconnaissance techniques. The US Army Rangers and the British Light Division both trace their origins back to Rogers and his Rangers. Rogers wrote 19 rules, which are all worth remembering:

* Don't forget nothing.

* Have your musket as clean as a whistle, hatchet scoured, 60 rounds, powder and ball and be ready to march at a minute's warning.

* When you're on the march, act the way you would if you was sneaking up on a deer. See the enemy first.

* Tell the truth about what you see and what you do. There is an army depending on us for correct information. You can lie all you please when you tell other folks about the Rangers, but never lie to a Ranger or officer.

* Don't never take a chance if you don't have to.

* When we're on the march, we march single file, far enough apart so one shot can't go through two men.

* If we strike swamps or soft ground, spread out abreast so it's hard to track us.

* When we march, we keep moving till dark to give the enemy the least possible chance at us.

* When we camp, half the party stays awake while the other half sleeps.

* If we take prisoners, we keep 'em separate till we have time to examine them, so they can't cook up a story between them.

* Don't ever march home the same way. Take a different route so you won't be ambushed.

* No matter whether we travel in big parties or little ones, each party has to keep a scout 20 yards on each flank and 20 yards in the rear, so the main body can't be surprised and wiped out.

* Every night you'll be told where to meet if surrounded by a superior force.

* Don't sit down to eat without posting sentries.

* Don't sleep beyond dawn. Dawn's when the French and Indians attack.

* Don't cross a river by a regular ford.

* If someone's trailing you, make a circle, come back on to your own tracks and ambush the folks that aim to ambush you.

* Don't stand up when the enemy's coming against you. Kneel down, lie down, hide behind a tree.

* Let the enemy come till he's almost close enough to touch. Then let him have it and jump out and finish him up with your hatchet.

Combat Report
Chad:
French Foreign Legion Mission

A former member of the French Foreign Legion describes a mission in Chad in 1983.

Fighting in Chad has been going on for the last 20 years, and the French Foreign Legion has been involved on numerous occasions. In 1983, rebels assisted by Libyan troops were having quite a bit of success against Chadian government forces. The French government decided to intervene, and so Legion paratroops and parts of my regiment moved to Chad to halt the rebel advance.

We arrived in Ndjamena in early July 1983 and began to acclimatise ourselves to the terrific heat. During this phase the high command was sussing out the strongest men for a mission that was being planned. After two weeks a group of eight of us were taken to a camp 20 miles from Ndjamena for intensive training: mainly night marches and using the map efficiently. It was because of my map reading that I earned my place with the final four chosen for the mission.

Locate and destroy

In the north of the FEBA (Forward Edge of Battle Area) our troops were having trouble with their radios. Intelligence had traced the problem to a jamming vehicle operating either near or just over the border with Niger: our mission was to locate and destroy this vehicle. Only four of us were to go in and do the work, but we had a team of eight others who would provide back-up.

After two days off, we moved off towards the border with Niger. We were to cover the last 10 miles on foot, during the day, in the oven-like heat, and this was greeted by a chorus of groans. We were to get into position by nightfall the following day, and watch the enemy for a day before moving in at 23.00 that night to do the job.

Next morning after breakfast we had a final check of equipment and made sure we carried no identification, so that if we were caught or killed they would not be able to trace us back to the Legion or the French army. By 08.30 we were on the trucks and moving off in the direction of the border and our drop-off point.

It didn't take too long to cover the distance, and we were soon out of the trucks, taking our bearings and heading off again. The sun was belting down and before long we were all panting and sweating and cursing.

The plan of assault

We took a break in a re-entrant, which had a few small scrub trees and some ledges. I found a nice place and lay down and dreamt of cold beer, ice cubes and cold showers. At about four in the afternoon we prepared to move out; the sun wasn't so fierce, although it wasn't exactly cool. Off we went at quite a pace, hoping to get the final few miles out of the way before nightfall.

As the evening drew in the air got cooler and out speed increased. I was knackered and my feet were sore and hot because of the uneven and rocky ground. By eight that evening we were at the border: the enemy vehicle was a mile or so on the other side, inside Niger.

We decided to leave our back-up eight to keep the border covered; that way they would be within striking distance to come and help us if we got stuck. The four of us, me, Jonke, Kovac and Champion, moved quietly and cautiously towards our objective. As we got closer we could see lights and hear noise from the target: good news, as it sounded like they weren't expecting visitors.

We moved to within 150 metres, where there was long dried grass and a few trees and scrub brush. It was good cover and would give us shade during the next day while we watched the enemy position to see how many soldiers were about.

When the sun came up we could see the vehicle bristling with aerials. It was next to the only house visible, which no doubt held enemy troops. But how many? All through the day we kept watch, counting six different men, which was good as we were expecting 10 at least.

By dusk we had a plan of assault ready. Everything was pre-arranged with our back-up: at 23.00 hours we would begin the assault, come what may. We noticed that five enemy had gone into the house and we supposed the sixth was in the vehicle working the jamming equipment. Jonko and I would take care of the vehicle while Kovac and Champion covered the building.

With about five minutes to go one of the soldiers came out of the house and came towards us. He was only going to the toilet, but if we waited until he finished and went back into the house we could be putting ourselves off schedule and possibly into danger.

I nodded to Jonko and drew my finger across my throat. He understood and moved off to intercept the soldier. A minute or so later he was back, giving me the thumbs-up sign. That made one less to worry about.

My heart was pumping

We then moved towards the vehicle. I went up to the front and Jonko moved towards the back. As I drew level with the cab, the driver's door opened and a soldier started to climb out! I nearly had a heart attack but soon recovered by diving on him and getting him in a headlock to stop him shouting out. We fell to the floor with him struggling like hell.

Jonko heard the door opening and came back to find us on the ground. Very quickly Jonko finished him off with his bayonet, then beckoned to me to follow him towards the back. My heart was pumping like mad.

Quickly I pulled the rear door open and Jonko stormed in, taking the operator completely by surprise. The vehicle was a mass of radio sets and maps. I immediately began to set up the explosives, and as soon as Jonko had dealt with the operator he helped me.

Then Jonko set the fuse for five minutes and we moved to leave the vehicle. Just as I reached the door another enemy soldier came towards it from the rear of the building. He looked stunned and moved for his weapon. I let off a burst of gunfire.

Now we had to move fast. We headed for the position we had been in all day. The other two kept us covered, and as the other enemy soldiers came out of the front of the house to see what was going on our lads opened up and cut them down: three of them, which made seven in all. We had miscounted by one and that nearly had put the whole operation in jeopardy. Luckily we had got away with it.

As soon as we were in position, we shouted for the others to move back through us. We watched the house and no-one else came out, so we got up and started running back towards the border and our back-up and, best of all, safety. I have never moved so quickly.

When we reached our back-up we stopped and it took me a good while to get my breath and calm down. Luckily there was no pursuit. The back-up had already signalled for the trucks, and as soon as they arrived we climbed aboard and drove with all speed away from the border. When we got back we were handed some ice cold beers, and I for one have never tasted anything sweeter.

Chadian soldiers in a village recaptured with French assistance; we were helping them in their war with Libyan-backed rebels. The heat was incredible: sometimes 120° in the shade.

We were trained in the use of explosives before we flew to Chad, teaching that was put to good use against the Libyans.

DOWN TO GEORGIA

The training course can be at squad, platoon or even company level, but no matter what the size of the group, the unit of instruction is the patrol. Rangers exist to go behind the enemy lines, get hold of something he's got and either deny it to him or bring it back for evaluation. It can be information about terrain and troop placements, it can be a railway bridge; makes no difference in the end to the way you set about 'obtaining' it. ("Well, okay, that particular railway bridge does look a little heavy. Guess we can't take it back with us. Better blow it up, huh?") In any event, and joking apart, the job at hand is long-range patrolling, and in the long run the best way to learn how to do it is to do it.

Patrolling all the way

You start out on patrol activity right away, and when day 58 comes around that's what you're still doing. The terrain will have changed; the patrol leaders will have changed (often!); some of the faces around you will have disappeared; the techniques you're using to achieve your aims and objectives will have changed to take account of local factors. But you'll still be there, patrolling.

The list of the basic skills a Ranger needs is a long one. Even the list of headings is a long one! Let's take a 'simple' case such as explosives and demolition. That means bangalore torpedoes, satchel charges, plastic; it means downing anything from a power line to a bridge; cratering roads and railbeds; demolishing buildings

The first phase of training involves confidence and obstacle courses – like walking a 20 cm beam, 10 metres up and airborne refresher courses for jump-trained men who have not recently parachuted. Strenuous PT sessions and hand-to-hand combat lessons complement an intensive period of training that teaches you demolitions, advanced airborne techniques, and medical techniques. However, the main emphasis, from the start, is patrolling. Navigation exercises again and again. Over very rough ground and at a remorseless pace.

By the time you go to Camp Benning and start leading patrols yourself, you are desperately tired and losing weight. Some students lose over 20 kilos as they subsist on occasional C-rations. The muscle-bound bodybuilders often fall by the wayside; the men who make the grade are often a lean 70 kilos and survive by sheer dedication.

A Ranger-trained soldier is not part of Special Forces as such. In fact, he is probably more valuable: an infantryman trained to a very exacting standard who will go back to his unit and provide high-grade leadership within the regular infantry battalions.

and destroying hardware; it means long-range detonation by radio and by wire; time pencils; trick detonators of all types.

That's only one area in which a Ranger has to be proficient. The rest can be grouped into logistics: movement techniques, including quite advanced mountain techniques and expedients; combat; escape and survival; and intelligence-gathering and transmission. Already, it starts to look impossible to get through such a list in just two months. But the on-the-job method that the Ranger School uses forces all trainees to combine skills quite effortlessly until that process becomes second nature.

The Georgia interior, around the Army Infantry Training School at Fort Benning, hard up against the Alabama State Line, where much of the course takes place, is hard country. Open fields, bramble-choked ravines and draws, swamps in the bottom-land. Definitely not a holiday resort. With the emphasis on secrecy and speed of movement, you can't just bull your way ahead, even if you have the strength, and this in itself is a valuable lesson. The ability to move clandestinely, after all, is a basic part of the Ranger's repertoire.

The first two patrols of the course are led by instructors and the two after that by students, with instructors

Left: The M16 rifle and 7.62-mm M60 GPMG are now supplemented in US Army infantry squads by the American version of the 5.56-mm Minimi light machine-gun. The combination gives US infantry unrivalled firepower.

Left: Operation Bushmaster, August 1971. L Company, 75th Rangers move away from the landing zone on a search and destroy mission. Unlike many units, the Rangers maintained a high standard of discipline as US troops were withdrawn from Vietnam.

Right (inset): Aerobics with weapons – a physical fitness course run by a Ranger team for US Army units stationed in West Germany. Many Ranger-trained personnel return to their units, so the Ranger course provides the Army with a steady stream of well-trained unit leaders.

This Ranger radio operator is armed with an M16A2 and a map of the Redesdale Training Area in Northumberland. In a recent live-firing exercise, the Rangers supplemented their already massive volume of small-arms fire with 90-mm recoilless rifles firing flechette rounds.

Fighting Fit

positioned to stop the action at any time and criticise what's going on. Then the graded patrols start, where students have to do it all for themselves without any help from the instructors. But they're there, constantly observing and marking. All these exercise patrols are going to count towards a trainee's final assessment mark. Basically, he has to achieve a high pass mark in more than half his activities to wear the Ranger badge, and should he fail the first week or so it's going to be very difficult to catch up. Most of the drop-outs occur, not surprisingly, in the first few weeks of the course.

It doesn't take long before the students catch on to the fact that the instructors are there to get them as much as to teach them, and then the whole attitude changes. Now, instead of looking to an instructor to see whether he thinks you're going about things the right way, you try to stay out of his sight, and do things your right way – and the righter you do it, of course, the more likely you are to be able to get away with it without him spotting you. The instructors have some unfair advantages: they don't need to stay in concealment and hump everything along with them. They use the roads, ride around in pick-up trucks and throw smoke and thunderflashes to let you know they've seen you. Hardly sporting. . .!

Trainees cross a rope bridge at Fort Benning, Georgia during the second stage of their Ranger training. Candidates can be forgiven for thinking that anything, real war included, must be easier than the unending strain of the training course.

Above: On exercise and in training you do not get much sleep in the Rangers. The 58-day training programme allows little more than an hour in a day of strenuous activity that usually ends in a prolonged unarmed combat session. Train hard, fight easy.

Below: A column of Rangers sets off for war. Note the chest webbing on the soldier second from left: this is to carry the 40-mm grenades for the M203 grenade launcher fitted to his M16A2 rifle.

Combat Report

Afghanistan:
Mujahideen Against Bandits

In 1980 I was part of a three-man team helping to train the Mujahideen, who were resisting the Soviet occupation in Afghanistan.

We were under strict instructions that on no account were we to get involved in combat, but it soon became clear that at least two of us would have to cross into Afghanistan to co-ordinate and assist with special tasks such as demolitions.

The first two such operations were successful and led to larger patrols being sent in, but by that time Soviet intelligence units were alerted to the possible presence of Westerners and there was a much larger presence of both Soviet and Afghan army units. So after a few hit and runs (shoot and scoot) we returned to our base camp and were debriefed, prior to returning to the UK.

Full reconnaissance

In 1983 I was asked if I was prepared to return to Afghanistan, alone and unrestricted. I would have no support, and should anything happen I was on my own.

I arrived at my old base camp in May 1983 and to my amazement found some of my old Mujahideen patrol still around. Quite a few, however, had been killed in action, or had fallen to a new hazard – bandits in the pay of the Soviets.

Intelligence was very sketchy, so a full reconnaissance was called for. I put together a patrol with a young Turk called Mohammed Khan, a survivor of all the last patrols and whose English was pretty fair, as second-in-command. We set out around the end of May, aiming for the power lines between Jagdalak and Kabul.

The snow had cleared a bit and the passes were open. We saw signs of horse-mounted patrols, possibly bandits, and after the second day in Afghanistan the Turk took the lead. He had been very good at this before and we reached the power lines still intact after some nine days' march. We took out three pylons and blacked out quite a lot of Jagdalak, and I obtained a fair amount of intelligence from villages as we passed through.

My worst fears realised

On the eleventh day we came across a party of very badly shot up Mujahideen, and it was quite clear that most of them would be dead within the next 24 hours. The Turk said that about six miles up ahead was a small village and that he would go ahead to prepare hot water etc for them. It was a good idea, but I told him to check it out very thoroughly.

The Turk and four others set off while I stayed with the wounded, using most of my medical kit on them. After about an hour we heard heavy firing in the direction of the village. Within two to three minutes all went quiet.

I hid the wounded, posted guards around them in a fairly well protected area of dense woodland, and set off with a party of six to see what was going on. We went some way off the track to avoid ambush and got within half a mile of the village. My worst fears were realised: bandits – about 18 to 20 of them. They had killed all of the Turk's party and had very badly mutilated the bodies, and were busy sorting out their spoils.

Night was falling but it seemed that they were making no attempt to move out. Our blood was running very high at this moment but to move in at this stage would be fatal. It was possible to approach the village from the high side via a gully, which I could see would take us to within 30 metres. The bandits' horses were in the centre and would also give us some cover.

I set up a cut-off group of four with one RPG and an RPD plus the bandits' own SKM along the only other way into the village. I left my Bergen with the cut-off group, having put all my mags for my AKM on my belt kit and grenades into the pockets of my windproof. It was at times like this that I wished I had a fully-trained patrol: house-clearing was not part of the Mujahideen training. I picked the two best I had; both spoke a little English.

I explained what I wanted them both to do. Basically, one, Hussain, was my back-up and the other one, Noor, was to cover our rear upon entry.

Darkness fell, and we made our way in. There was no sentry as such, but we took no chances. I came out of the gully and across to the first building, then Hussain, then Noor; slowly we made our way to the window. As is common, there was no electric lighting or power, but there was a fire burning and I could see a group sitting around it with eight or nine weapons all in a heap.

House clearing

We checked out the building next door, then I noticed some more horses at the rear of a building. I made my way over there and found a large group sitting around interrogating some poor soul. He was unknown to us – most likely an Afghan army deserter who had found the Mujahideen and had got himself taken alive.

I made a rough count; we had found around 35 so far, and on further searching we found three more asleep in a hut with a pile of stores, obviously booty from other unfortunates. I entered the hut and dispatched all three while they slept, still clutching their weapons.

I was having trouble holding both Hussain and Noor back, so I sent Noor with four grenades to take out the two small houses, with instructions: two grenades in each – but stay outside. He said he understood, and off he went. By this time it was around 01.00 hours, the moon was high, and light was good.

I pulled two grenades out and waited; two large explosions shook the night. I tossed mine, and two more explosions followed my two. I immediately leapt through the window, firing at a person crawling towards his weapon, and Hussain followed me. I dispatched three more, checking around the house – all occupants were dead. We then heard a burst of automatic followed by some small arms fire.

Only one grenade left . . .

I had only one grenade left. I changed mags and also checked Hussain. Noor was under fire from both buildings. We ran to the rear of the second building but it had no windows or doors to the rear so it had to be a front attack again. I tossed in the grenade, and the explosion ripped the front out. I raced in, giving three sharp bursts at targets; they all dropped without returning any fire.

Fire was still pouring out of the other house towards Noor, who was now at the entry to the gully and returning a small amount of fire. I shouted for him to stop firing. I could hear the

Me and the team. Note the new AKM 7.62×39 assault rifle and the RPG-7 rocket launcher. The language barrier was a big problem, as was the Mujahideen lack of training.

bandits' voices quite clearly, and leapt straight through the window firing in all directions.

There was all hell let loose and Hussain caught a round which went straight through a muscle in his left arm. I stopped the blood and was just about to leave when I noticed movement on the roof to the left of me. I let off a burst, and over went a young lad of about 15 armed with a PSh41 sub-machine gun.

Then we heard firing from the direction of the cut-off position, followed by the whoosh of the RPG, an explosion and then quiet. When we reached them we found two enemy dead on the track and the remains of three or four others. I put the total at 41 dead, no wounded; we had four dead and one, Hussain, wounded.

We made it back over to our base camp without further incident, and Hussain had the full attention of the camp. I wished I was a fly on the wall in the Soviet ops room; the incident must had been quite a shock to them, but it was a great morale booster to the Mujahideen.

On the move with the local transport, on an infiltration route into Afghanistan. Crossing the mountain passes, there was always the threat of air attack, anti-personnel mines or ambush by Spetsnaz special forces.

WAY TO GO

After nearly three weeks at Fort Benning, the trainees are off to the mountains. To Camp Frank Merrill, to be precise, on the southern flanks of the Blue Ridge Mountains. Now the patrols get longer, the travelling harder, the special skills more physically demanding.

As well as 'ordinary' cross-country movement, there are now the problems of scaling and descending cliffs, crossing ravines and generally living where the land goes straight up as often as it goes straight on. And, of course, there are still objectives to be mapped, troop movements to be observed, installations to be destroyed...all that usual old Ranger crap. No wonder some of the students don't know where or who they are by this stage.

Endless exercise

There's no fixed schedule at all by now, and one exercise just blends in with another without any sign, except perhaps a change of roles. The instructors now give their orders in just the form that any working Ranger patrol would expect to receive them, and it's up to the trainees themselves to carry out the mission as best they can and in the way they see fit. Of course, there are the guys in the pick-up truck, the guys sunning themselves on the rocks over there, the guys with the thunderflashes to give you immediate notice that you've screwed up...

Three weeks of this particular hell and it's up sticks and off to find a dif-

Mountain training

The mountain phase concentrates on recon. patrols, and the individual missions are a little longer than at Camp Benning. You learn mountaineering skills, which include jollies like casualty evacuation down cliffs and a 75-metre rappel at night. The constant lack of sleep is a serious problem for all of you, eating away at your concentration. You have to fight the tiredness all the time to avoid making costly mistakes. In one widely-reported incident a student found himself trying to put an imaginary coin in the side of a tree which he mistook for a drinks machine. Hallucinations are all too common if you've been without sleep for too long, and you must master it or fail the course.

ferent species of it, in the swamps around Eglin Air Force Base in Florida. And how do they travel? By bus? By truck, even? Well, not quite. They go by air, but hardly in Club Class. The embarkation is from a Georgia dirt road, at night, into a C-130 Hercules – not the world's most comfortable aircraft – and the landing is by parachute. Once you've arrived (at the corner of Eglin AFB known as Camp James E. Rudder), you're combat-ready right from the moment your feet touch the ground.

It doesn't seem to matter to anyone, except perhaps the trainee, that much of this land is under four or five feet of water. The patrolling still has to continue; there are still objectives out there, and there will always be intelligence officers who'll want to know about them.

It's been seven weeks now, and the men on the course are starting to show very serious signs of fatigue. This is much harder work, over such a sustained period, than any Ranger would normally be expected to undertake in combat. It's not unusual for big men to lose 40 or 50 pounds in weight during the Ranger School.

All through the course, the men have been using helicopters as a regular part of their lives. In Florida

These Rangers, on the move across the barren wastes of the Otterburn training area, have literally just dropped in from the USA. Their basic weapon is the M16A2, which fires the new NATO SS109 round.

Left: A Ranger company advances to contact, with two platoons up and one in reserve. True to form, the Rangers left their sleeping bags back in America in favour of carrying more ammunition for a live firing attack.

Right: Ranger endurance is based on exceptional levels of physical fitness. Rangers are pushed to and beyond exhaustion and then tested to see if they can still complete their mission on long exercises.

*For serious bunker-busting you need something a little larger than a 66-mm, and the Rangers have held on to their M67 90-mm recoilless rifles firing a **HEAT** warhead and a flechette anti-personnel round. Rangers believe in firepower.*

Ranger training is designed to build complete confidence in the individual that he can and will achieve any task. Vaguely dangerous exercises like this aerial ropeway help to build that confidence.

they add another mode of transport – the RB-15 rubber boat. They also get to know how to work with another kind of artillery, besides the 105-mm and 155-mm howitzers they've been FO'ing for – the Spectre gunships, themselves based at Eglin. Best to learn in training what all that ordnance feels like, hitting just yards away from your own position, and best to learn, too, just how much confidence can be placed in modern fire-control systems like that of the AC-130U gunships.

Five-part task

As a simplification, the Ranger's task can be split into five parts: briefing, movement to objective, doing the job, recovery, and de-briefing. Unless each segment is carried out properly, the mission is going to be a failure: like everything else, a Ranger mission is as strong as its weakest point, and no stronger. The training course aims to strengthen up those weaknesses and work on the strengths until the finished product is a man with the self-confidence and the abilities to live safely in country held by an aggressive enemy without ever being in too much danger. There's no price too high to pay for that feeling.

Above: A Ranger platoon commander briefs his lead section commander on the next leg of the advance to an attack on a mock-up airfield, complete with real aircraft. Note that both he and his radio operator carry radios.

Below: Support weapons platoon prepare to move up to a fire support position for the attack. Note the 40-mm underbarrel grenade-launcher carried by this member of a Ranger mortar platoon. Rangers are trained on a wide range of weapons, both domestic and foreign.

Jungle training

You actually get eight hours' sleep before parachuting into Eglin Air Force Base, Florida, for your swamp and jungle training phase. This 'luxury' is imposed by Army regulations, since mentally and physically exhausted men will suffer unacceptably high casualties if they attempt a parachute drop. But once you're in the Florida swamps, generally in 1½ metres of water, you have reached the toughest part of the course. The effect of the earlier training has left you tired and the strain of 18 days in the swamps is indescribable.

Good personal admin. is obviously vital on long-range patrolling behind enemy lines. Constantly wet-through during the missions in the swamps, you wage a never-ending battle against trench foot and other medical problems. You must know how to look after yourself.

The final exercises in Florida involve helicopter rappels from about 20 metres and co-ordinated action with Air Force strike aircraft. The scenario is that you are behind enemy lines and friendly forces are advancing, driving the opposition back towards you. You use hit-and-run tactics, holing up by day and raiding every night. The exercises are very realistic and many of the candidates are so spaced out that they think they are actually at war.